General Mitchell with H. R. H. Prince of Wales Before Their Flight Over the Rhine and Moselle Rivers. The Prince Was the First Member of a Reigning Family to Fly Across the Rhine

SKYWAYS

SKYWAYS

A BOOK ON MODERN AERONAUTICS

BY GENERAL WILLIAM MITCHELL

FORMER COMMANDER
AIR FORCES, A. E. F.
AND DIRECTOR
MILITARY AERONAUTICS
U. S. ARMY, AUTHOR OF
"WINGED DEFENSE"

1 9 3 0
Philadelphia
and London

J. B. LIPPINCOTT COMPANY

COPYRIGHT 1930
BY WILLIAM MITCHELL

PRINTED IN THE U. S. A.

DEDICATION

I dedicate this book to my two little children, Lucy Trumbull and William, Junior, who in their lifetime will see aeronautics become the greatest and principal means of national defense and rapid transportation all over the world, and possibly beyond our world into interstellar space.

FOREWORD

THE book "Skyways," written at the request of many of my friends, deals in a simple, elementary way with the subject of aeronautics as it exists at present and as it is applied in the various countries of the world. It contains information on all branches of aeronautics, civil, commercial and military, and also includes many personal experiences connected with aviation in various parts of the world.

More than three decades ago, I entered the Signal Corps of the United States Army, which at that time was charged with handling aeronautics for the Government. Thirty years ago I studied for my examination for promotion in a little log cabin we had built on the Good Pasture River in northern Alaska, where we were then laying telegraph lines through that great territory. The principal part of our aeronautical examination dealt with spherical and "sausage" balloons, how they were built, how they were handled from the ground as elevated platforms, from which a much broader view could be obtained than by any other means; how free balloons were used and how hydrogen gas could be made and applied to the balloons

FOREWORD

with improvised materials. We had data on the gliding experiments of Lilienthal and Chanute, a little information on Prof. Langley's attempts at heavier-than-air flight. We knew about Santos-Dumont's airships, and the attempts of Count Zeppelin to create a great dirigible. Opposed to this, we had Prof. Simon Newcomb's data, in which he proved, to his own satisfaction at least, that mechanical flight was impossible.

With the few materials we had at hand we made kites, then put them in tandem and finally evolved a structure that would lift a man. It was able to carry wire into the air for over a mile. In 1904, on this kite, we used the first radio instruments of the United States Army and at Fort Leavenworth, Kansas, we received a radio message from the steamer "Naverisk," 1900 miles away in San Juan Harbor in Porto Rico, which was the world's record for distance in radio at that time. Flying and radio have gone hand in hand ever since.

Shortly after this, the Wrights' work with their heavier-than-air machines came to our notice and was carefully followed. Our Signal Corps obtained and operated the first airplane that the Wrights sold.

Flying was never particularly popular in the army. Persons who desired to fly were looked on

FOREWORD

as lacking something in their mentality. I learned to fly while on duty with the General Staff in Washington. I would take the boat down the Potomac on Saturday night to Newport News, where Glenn Curtiss had established a little flying school, fly all day Sunday, and be back at my desk in the Army War College on Monday morning. After four days of this instruction, I was "turned loose" for my first solo flight. I knew practically nothing about flying. Fortunately, I cracked up the machine in making a bad landing, which taught me more than anything that ever happened to me in the air.

For many years I had the opportunity of developing things aeronautical in the government service. I commanded the biggest air force ever used in war and have had the privilege and opportunity of flying in practically all the countries in the northern hemisphere. This source of knowledge and experience has been drawn upon in the make-up of this book. I have tried to make it understandable to both young and old, and each year I intend to revise, improve and bring it up to date.

The field for exploration and adventure and things new may be narrowing on the earth's surface but the air and the sky offer a boundless future to daring spirits that wish to rise into it.

Contents

1 – Man Flies	17
2 – Engines	31
3 – Learning to Fly	51
4 – Kind of Men to Make into Pilots	63
5 – Weather	72
6 – Flying Fields and Airways	92
7 – Commercial Aviation	107
8 – Instruments	120
9 – Safety Devices	135
10 – Maps	145
11 – How the Surface of the Earth Looks from the Air	157
12 – Airplane Maneuvers	167
13 – Airships	180
14 – Sporting Side of Aviation	195
15 – A Modern Air Liner	217
16 – A Glance at World Aeronautics	235
17 – Military Aviation	253
18 – Use of Aircraft in War	271
19 – Aeronautical Law	290
20 – Aviation of the Future	299
Index	311

Illustrations

General Mitchell with H.R.H. Prince of Wales	*Frontispiece*
The Langley Airplane Designed in the Late Nineties of the Last Century	18
Parts of a Military Airplane	19
The De Bothezat Heliocopter	24
The Cierva Autogyro Landing Vertically on a Line	25
The Cierva Autogyro in Full Flight	25
A Supercharged Engine Installation	38
Packard Diesel Aircraft Engine	39
Device for Teaching a Pilot How to Use the Controls	52
Equipment on a Transcontinental Flying Field	100
Floodlights Illuminating an Airdrome at Night	101
Early Aerial Torpedo Launched Successfully without Human Pilot in 1917	132
Pilot Equipped for High Altitude Flying	133
Six Men Jumping from Three Airplanes Simultaneously	140
The Verville Air Coach	141
Refueling Planes While in the Air	141
French Airplane Equipped with Slotted Wings	144
Photograph Taken from an Altitude of Eighteen Thousand Feet Across Lake Erie	145
Strip Map for the Use of Air Pilots	148
Blackboard for Noting Weather Conditions	149
Airplanes are Used in Patrolling Forests to Guard Against Fires	160
Airplane "Dusting" an Orchard	161
The Loop	170
The Spin or Vrille	171
The Roll or Barrel	172
The Half Roll	173

ILLUSTRATIONS

The Chandelle	174
The Renversement	175
Airline Distance Between Centers of Population	186
Mrs. Mitchell, Dr. Eckener, and Captain Lehmann During an Inspection of the Zeppelin Works	187
Cross Section of the Graf Zeppelin	188
Graf Zeppelin Showing the Two Keels, One at the Bottom, One Two Thirds of the Way Up	189
Glider Attached to an Airplane	192
Cabin of an Airship with a Device for Carrying Airplane Underneath	193
Landing in Deep Snow at Camp Borden, Canada	200
General Mitchell Taking Off in an Airplane Equipped with Skis	200
Ezra Meeker, Who Crossed the Continent by Ox Team Sixty Years Ago	201
General Mitchell Taking General Aguinaldo for a Trip in the Air	210
Manila, P. I., from the Air	210
King Lucas of the Negritos and Some of His Tribe	211
General and Mrs. Mitchell with King Lucas and His Queen	211
Commercial Airplane of the German Luft-Hansa	230
The Great French Airport of Le Bourget, France	231
An Italian Caproni Airplane Being set Up in the Factory at Milan	242
The Newest Travel Service Single-Seater Pursuit Airplane, The Bernard 20 Cl	243
Swedish Three-Seater All Purpose Military Airplane of Metal Construction	243
The Dornier DO-X, the World's Largest Airplane	244
Mr. Dornier, Dr. Eckener, and General Mitchell Standing in Front of a Dornier Airplane	245
General and Mrs. Mitchell Visiting the Siamese Air Force in Bangkok	250
Part of America's Last Air Force Assembled at Langley Field in 1921	251

ILLUSTRATIONS

Barling Bomber in Flight	252
The Barling Bomber, the Largest Practical Airplane Ever Built in the United States	252
A Construction Representing the Skyline of a City Being Bombed by Airplanes	262
Smoke Curtain Over New York Laid by an Airplane Showing How Gas Curtains Can Be Laid Which Will Drift Over Large Cities for Twenty or Thirty Minutes	262
A Smoke or Gas Curtain Being Laid To Cover a Warship	263
Four Twenty-Five-Pound Bombs Hitting Ship	264
Thirty Seconds after the Phosphorous Bombs Hit the Battleship	264
The Battleship as the Bomb Hit Her	265
Battleship After Being Hit by an Eleven-Hundred-Pound High Explosive Bomb	265
Direct Hit by an Eleven-Hundred-Pound Bomb on a Battleship	266
A Four-Thousand-Pound Bomb, Man's Greatest Weapon	267
Bombing Planes in Action	272
General Mitchell Beside a Pursuit Plane	273
British Pursuit Airplane, The "Partridge"	276
British Single-Seater Pursuit Plane, The "Bristol"	276
Bombardment Squadron in Flight	277
Anti-Aircraft Searchlights	288
Modern Anti-Aircraft Battery Being Put in Position	288
Four Dirigible Airships in Formation Over Langley Field	289
The New Junkers 2400 H.P. Airplane G-38	304
Another View of the New Junkers Airplane G-38	305
Little Eight H.P. Plane That Flew from Dayton to Columbus, Ohio, on Two and One-Half Gallons of Gasoline	306
The Shrinking Map due to Reduction of Distances by Airplane	307

SKYWAYS

CHAPTER I

MAN FLIES

WE HUMAN beings fly. We have launched ourselves into what we call the air, a fluid that covers the whole earth like a deep blanket. Wherever this blanket extends, there we can go. As it covers the whole world, all places are accessible to the flyer.

People have always wanted to fly and have tried to from time immemorial. They have watched the birds and tried to copy them. They have watched the bat and the flying squirrel, insects and the flying fish. But man could never even approach the means that these animals had for taking them through the air, because he had nothing strong enough to pull him through it in proportion to his weight, until the arrival of the gasoline engine. Then, instead of flapping his way through the air, he constructed an air propellor, built according to the same principle as a water propellor, and hitched it to his engine. A bird or an animal could not possibly parallel this type of motive power, because there are no rotary joints, or joints that turn around, in any living creature. Propellors give more power and are really more efficient than the wings of birds. We attain speeds so great with our aircraft that the body of a bird would be broken to pieces and its feathers all blown out if it approached these rates.

This fluid into which we have projected ourselves is strange to us, even more strange than was the water to our ancestors when they first went out in boats. If a person falls into the sea, his weight is almost the same as that of the water, in fact some water is even heavier than a man's body and holds him up without effort. But if a man falls into the air from a height, unless he is supported by a plane, a parachute or a balloon, he will go straight to the earth with terrific speed and break all to pieces when he strikes it.

We have only been flying for about twenty-five years. Each year we learn more about it, we go faster, higher and for greater distances without landing. Now aircraft have to be built so that people can live in them, just as ships at sea have their cabins, kitchens and living rooms.

The airplane may be likened to a stone that is skipped over the water. The stone must be thrown with a certain force and speed to keep above the water. If it slows down, as it is heavier than the water, it will immediately sink. In the same way, an airplane has to move just so fast through the air and cover a certain number of particles of air

The Langley Airplane Designed in the Late Nineties of the Last Century

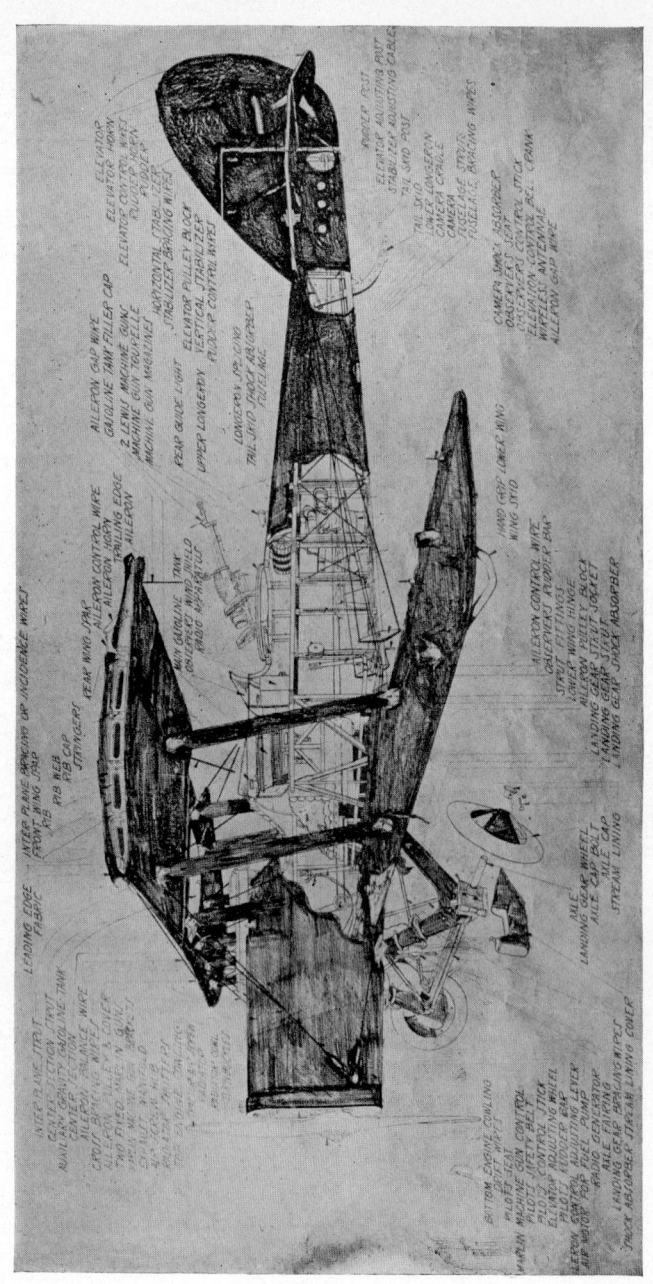

PARTS OF A MILITARY AIRPLANE

in a certain time to keep itself up, otherwise it will fall through the air to the earth. The contrivance that gives it speed is the motor, attached to the propellor. The propellor may push the airplane or it may pull it. The airplane is held up or·sustained in the air by its wings, which may be likened to the under surface of the stone skipped across the water. The airplane may have one, two or three wings, and is called a monoplane, biplane, triplane, or where there are more than three wings, a multiplane.

Besides the wings themselves as the principal means of sustentation, the airplane has a body, or fuselage, which connects the wings with the control surfaces. These control surfaces, which are used to guide it to the right or left, or up and down, have to be situated at some distance from the wings so that the eddy currents of air produced behind the wings when in flight will not affect them. If they are too close to the wings, these control surfaces may be put into "dead" air when the airplane is in certain positions, so that they will not work. The ordinary rule of thumb for calculating the distance the rudder and elevators should be from the wing so they will not be affected by the air turbulence, is two and a half times the chord of the wing. The chord is the distance across the wing, its width, from the leading edge to the trailing edge. If you see an airplane in which the control surfaces are not this far back of the wing, the chances are it will be difficult to handle in certain positions assumed in the air.

The airplane is guided to right or left by a rudder, which is much the same as the rudder on a boat. The elevators incline the airplane up and down. They are really horizontal rudders that steer the plane up or down, just as the vertical rudder steers to left or right.

One unique function possessed by the airplane, which is required by no other vehicle, is the power to put one wing up or down, or "bank" the plane. In developing the airplane, it was found necessary when making a turn to keep all its under surface in contact with the air. If a turn was made without sufficient air under the wings, the plane would slip sideways, perhaps turn over and stall. The ailerons, or little wings, which accomplish this purpose are sections of the main wings, out near the tip, where they have the most effect on the air. If a turn is to be made to the left, the aileron on the right wing is pushed down and at the same time the aileron on the left wing is pulled up. The action of the air on these surfaces will then throw the right wing up and the left wing down.

The shapes of the wings are important. Some offer much more resistance to the air than others. When the airplane is in flight, not only does the air hold it up from underneath but a vacuum is created on the top of the wing which tends to suck the airplane up into it, thereby giving it more support. At first consideration, one might think that a round ball would offer the least resistance to the air when passing through it; but if a cannon ball is dropped from high in the air, it does not fall straight but zigzags from side to side, because a vacuum is created behind it which pulls it from one side to the other. However, if we drop a projectile that is pear or egg-shaped, we find that it goes almost exactly straight, because the elongated end causes the air to slip around and leave it without creating a vacuum.

All parts of an airplane affected by the air stream are shaped more or less like a thin pear or egg. This is called a streamline form, so designated from the shapes one may observe in beds of streams. Behind the stones over which the water flows one often sees little egg-shaped ridges of sand. These have been built up gradually to prevent the water from rushing in behind the stones and creating eddies. A streamline form on an airplane is much more pleasing to the eye than a round or blunt shape. After a slight acquaintance with airplanes, one can readily tell which will be fastest and best in the air merely by looking at the shapes.

Every airplane has a certain speed which it must maintain to keep in the air. A very large plane with a light load is able to go much slower than a very small one with a heavy load. This minimum speed is known as "stalling speed" or "landing speed," and is always the same for the same kind of airplane.

It might be said that an airplane can have two kinds of speed, one due to its motor pulling it through the air, and the other to the force of gravity which pulls it toward the earth. The limiting speed of the average small airplane pulled by its motor is around 100 miles per hour. If this plane falls toward the ground, it will continue increasing in speed until it reaches the point where the resistance of the air is such that it can fall no faster. It makes no difference if propellor and engine are going full speed, this speed cannot be increased as the air holds it up. The maximum speed of fall of such an airplane might be around 250 miles per hour. If there were no air and the plane were falling through space, it would continue to fall faster and faster; but in our atmosphere, the air forms a cushion in front of it which cannot be pierced. Airplanes should be constructed strong enough to withstand not only the speed given them by their engine, but also this maximum speed, or "terminal velocity," if they fall to earth.

The modern airplane is not a structure which has been evolved in a short time, but is the result of hundreds of years of experiment and trial. Kites, windmills, balloons and parachutes, even the flight of the arrow with its winged shaft, have all contributed to its development. Gliders in which people have soared through the air without a motor have done more than anything else toward the solution of the problems of flight. Possibly many legends like the flying carpet of the Arabian Nights, or Pegasus, or Icarus, had a foundation in gliders which human beings built and used from mountains or hills.

During the last generation, the gliders of Chanute and Lillienthal solved almost all the problems of flight except that of the aileron; so when the gasoline engine came along and the Wright brothers applied it to the first mechanically propelled airplane in 1903, conditions were ready for the world to take up flying.

The first successful airplane of the Wrights contained all the principal parts that a modern plane has. Their landing gear and method of controlling the various surfaces, although somewhat different in mechanical arrangement from those now in use, were essentially the same. The development of the airplane has tended toward greater size, speed, power and comfort, but it is a question whether the airplane of today is any safer than were some of those constructed by the Wrights.

Besides the airplane, there is another kind of heavier-than-air flying machine, called the helicopter. As an airplane has to glide along the earth for a certain distance to get enough speed to lift itself, it requires a large field for its use. Such fields are difficult to find in the centers of cities, in forests or mountains. Inventors have tried to make a flying machine which would rise perpendicularly from a place like the top of a building. In order to accomplish this, it has been necessary to make a propellor that gives a pull straight up and until recently it was difficult to get an engine strong enough for this. This type of flying machine could not have big wings placed horizontally, or parallel to the ground, because they would offer too much resistance to the passage of the machine straight up. At first a good deal of difficulty was encountered by the inventors in getting a machine of this kind stable enough, that did not fall to one side or the other, and that could be directed or guided in the

The De Bothezat Heliocopter

The Cierva Autogyro Landing Vertically on a Line

The Cierva Autogyro in Full Flight

direction desired. Also, if a machine with just a propellor to pull it straight up in the air had a motor stoppage, it would fall straight to the earth as there would be no wings to support it as an airplane has. The pilot would have no chance to get out and spread his parachute as the big propellor would be in his way. These things have been gradually overcome, and modern helicopters are able to rise from the ground and after attaining a certain altitude, to go in any direction desired.

Nearly all of them have a large propellor which acts around a vertical axis, that is, the propellor is horizontal with the earth. Some also have a smaller propellor like that of an airplane, which acts when it is desired to go in a horizontal direction. The big propellor is shaped so that it acts like a supporting wing. There are small wings which can be inclined up or down, so that when the helicopter rises, these can be placed vertically and will not hold back the machine. Then when horizontal flight is started, they can be set horizontally and exert their support. While helicopters have not yet been entirely perfected, they have gone far enough so that we believe they will ultimately be successful.

A very interesting type of heavier-than-air craft is the Cierva autogyro. It is neither a helicopter nor an airplane. It consists of a body or fuselage very similar to that of an airplane. In its nose there is a motor and the ordinary type of airplane propellor. Its small stubby wings and tail surfaces are somewhat similar to those of an airplane. The remarkable feature of this machine is the windmill or rotary wing which is mounted over it. This windmill, or rotor as it is called, is not actuated directly by any power from the engine but is made to revolve by the airstream from the propellor striking against it. When an ordinary airplane takes off in flight, its propellor gives it speed through the air and makes air pass under the wing at such a rapid rate that the airplane rises. With the autogyro, instead of the wing being fixed in position, it rotates and goes through as many particles of air in a given time as the wing of an airplane does; but with the windmill, instead of a great deal of forward motion being required, it is accomplished in one place by rotation.

The autogyro is flown much the same as an airplane; the pilot gets in, the motor is started, the propellor revolves and then the rotor on top of the structure begins to act and the machine moves across the field. When the speed of rotation of the windmill is fast enough, it takes off into the air. Its stability is remarkable. The weights are hung so low, compared to the rotating wing above, that the effect is very much like that of a person in a parachute.

The machine can be made to hover over a certain place when climbing it upward. It can be brought straight down to the ground and landed on a place without any forward motion. If the motor fails, the windmill keeps on turning and breaks the fall toward the ground so that the impact is not sufficient to break up the machine. The faster the machine falls, the more rapidly the windmill rotates; and the more rapidly it rotates, the more it supports the machine and slows it up. The autogyro has been very successful in its flights and promises a great deal for the future, where machines are required to land on the top of a building, a small field, in a forest or the top of a mountain. It can be used to fly at very low altitudes, within a few feet of the ground. If anything happens to the motor, it comes down slowly and does not smash up. In case of motor stoppage to an airplane at low altitude, it would have to glide into whatever was in front of it, whether a forest, broken ground, high tension electric wires or some other danger, whereas the autogyro can be brought down vertically at a safe speed. It is beginning to be manufactured on a commercial basis.

The foremost representative of lighter-than-air

craft is the airship, which is a descendant of the balloon. A long period of development took place before the great airships that cross the seas today and fly around the world were developed. Many centuries ago, people filled very light bags full of hot air over a fire, and as the heated air was much lighter than the cold air about it, these balloons rose to quite a height. Many of us as children had tissue paper balloons, at the bottom of which was cotton saturated with oil, to which we set fire. This would heat the air in the balloon and it would float off through the air.

In 1789, the Montgolfier brothers in France began putting hydrogen gas, which is lighter than air, into balloons and were able to make trips of considerable length, but as they had no means of propelling their craft, they had to go wherever the wind took them. Not only after the gasoline engine made its appearance, it was put into lighter-than-air ships, particularly by the Germans, the French and the Italians.

At first, ordinary bags were used to contain the gas, but when these were pushed through the air rapidly, the pressure changed their shape, making the bag weaker in one place than another and causing accidents. Various expedients were used to overcome this by making the dirigible balloon in sections, by equipping it with rigid frames and by making its shape streamline.

The present airship, evolved during the last thirty years, has a rigid framework of metal over which an outside covering of either fabric or metal is stretched. Inside this frame are placed a number of balloons that contain hydrogen or other gas that lifts the airship from the ground.

Gas expands and contracts very rapidly in accordance with the temperature. Many experiments had to be made before finding out how much gas should be put into the balloons so that a great deal would not be lost by valving. This has all been worked out now, and the balloons inside the outer envelope are filled with only enough gas to keep them up, but not enough so that if the gas is heated, some will have to be released.

Instead of gasoline or oil, airships now burn a gas in their engines which has the same weight as air. With this, the weight of the airship does not fluctuate; when this gas is used up, air takes its place. This marks a great advance in airship development. Without the use of a gas of this kind, the Zeppelin that recently completed the round-the-world trip would have had great difficulty in making the voyage.

Airships are very large and comfortable. They

SKYWAYS have almost as much room in them as an ocean steamer and they go about four times as fast. They will be made to go much faster still and within a few years we shall undoubtedly see airship lines from America to Europe and to Asia.

CHAPTER II

ENGINES

THE instrument that pulls an airplane through the air is its propellor, but this has to be actuated and driven by a source of power, the motor, which is the most important element in the airplane.

The invention of the internal combustion engine by the Germans, Otto and Daimler, during the seventies of the last century, made flying possible. This engine, as its name implies, is a machine in which an explosion takes place, which is harnessed up to do useful work. It might be compared to a battery of artillery of from six to twelve pieces, firing away under the hood of the airplane. Suppose six cannon were set up in line, each firing into a wheel like the ordinary water wheel, with each wheel connected to one shaft. A man is at each cannon; one loads Number One with a cartridge and pulls the trigger; Number Two is ready to fire immediately after Number One is through, and Numbers Three, Four, Five and Six act correspondingly. By the time Number Six has fired, Number One is ready again and so on. This is what an internal combustion engine is like, and this power is connected up and transmitted through a very complicated system of machinery, to the propellor of an airplane, or to the wheels of an automobile, to belting or other means of utilizing power.

The gasoline engine is one of the most complicated machines ever devised. During the Middle Ages, very intricate mechanical toys were made, which had hundreds and hundreds of parts. Some were fashioned to represent people, and had movable arms and legs, head and eyes. They were marvels of ingenuity but even they could not be compared to the modern gasoline engine, in which there are thousands of parts. The ordinary aeronautical engine of this type has from twenty-five hundred to six thousand parts. The speed of motion of these parts requires a most careful system of oiling. If for an instant lubrication fails, the metal parts become hot and may melt, some pin or joint that holds a moving part breaks and is thrown out with a whirling motion that tears up the whole contrivance and may even shatter the case of the motor.

The cylinders of the engine, where the explosions take place, may be likened to the barrel of a cannon. They are enormously strong chambers into which a mixture of oxygen and gasoline, or other explosive substances, is sprayed, then compressed to the point where it will give the maximum explosion. It is ignited by an electric spark and the resultant explosion drives out what is called a piston, or stopper inserted in the cylinder. When pushed out, it connects with a crank which it moves through a part of a circle. Each cylinder takes up the explosion as the previous one leaves off, and its piston pushes the crank through another part of the arc, so that a continuous source of power is obtained.

The electric spark which ignites the mixture is turned on at the proper instant of compression by a system of cams which act in the same way as a man pulling the trigger of a gun. A cam is a projection or knob sticking out from a rod or shaft and as this shaft is turned over, these cams touch the instrument they are designed to work. The ignition cam takes the form of a round disk which contains the ends of the wires of the electric circuit. As this machinery turns around, one after the other the contact points touch the wire that goes to each cylinder, which makes the spark and explodes the mixture.

At the same time, another cam acts on a valve, or little door into the cylinder, which admits the mixture of gasoline and air. Still another cam opens a valve to let the gas out of the cylinder after it has been exploded.

The instrument that mixes the gasoline and air

is called a carburetor. It is a chamber arranged to feed the right proportion of gasoline and air into the cylinders. It is here, we may say, that the cartridges are made to put into our guns, or cylinders. The pistons are the projectiles shot out and the electrical ignition system the trigger which fires the charge.

The heat of combustion in the motor is so great that it must be cooled either by large radiating surfaces on which the air can impinge, or by the circulation of a liquid around its cylinders which in turn is cooled in a radiator through which cold air passes.

Since its invention, the gasoline engine has changed very little in principle. It has been refined, simplified and made considerably lighter. It has been made into various forms, either with the cylinders in line or arranged in the shape of a V, similar to automobile engines in general use. Radial engines, whose cylinders are arranged in the form of a star around the main shaft, are widely used. The engine itself may revolve while the shaft is stationary, the propellor being connected directly to the engine; or the cylinders may remain fixed in position and the shaft in the middle driven around. The former type is known as a rotary engine. They must of course be air cooled. In the early development of aviation, they were very good because they could be made so light. As more and more power was required and engines had to be made larger, the rotary engines were not so practical, as in the larger sizes it was hard to compensate for the expansion and contraction of the metal in various parts, besides other difficulties. A very serious impediment was found in the gyroscopic action which resulted from the swift whirling of a heavy mass of metal. During the last few years, the rotary engine has not been used as much as formerly.

The popularity of the radial engine has increased, principally because it is more easily cooled by air than a vertical engine whose cylinders are placed one behind the other. All the cylinders of a radial engine can be exposed at one time to the flow of air. Of course there are advantages and disadvantages in all the various forms engines have taken. Air cooled engines can be made somewhat simpler and lighter than the liquid cooled types. The radial engine is easy to mount on an airplane, as it is not very long from front to rear. It is easy to inspect because it is so flat. It requires no liquid for cooling. On the other hand, it is very broad in diameter and offers a great deal of resistance to the air. The lubrication of certain parts, such as the end of rocker arms and cams, is more difficult than in other forms of engines. As it must be exposed to the outside air in order to be cooled, it cannot be set back in an engine room, as can be done with liquid cooled engines.

It is difficult to make air cooled engines in very large sizes, around 1000 horsepower, as the difference in the expansion and contraction of the pistons and cylinders and other parts is so great as to cause a very uneconomical loss of power. Of course, radial engines might be cooled by a liquid, but this would neutralize their other advantages. Formerly when the only cooling medium was water, which boiled over, evaporated and froze, the radial engine had a greater advantage than at present when we have such liquids as ethylene glycol, whose boiling point is 335 degrees Fahrenheit, as against 212 degrees in water, whose initial freezing point is zero but which does not freeze solid until 45 degrees below zero is reached. Such liquids are not easily evaporated. This has made it possible to reduce the size of the radiator considerably, as well as the amount of cooling agent carried, consequently the airplane gives a superior performance, especially as regards speed.

As an airplane ascends, the air which the engine encounters contains less and less oxygen, until at an altitude of about 20,000 feet, the oxygen content

ENGINES

is so scant that the average engine has difficulty in functioning. So a means must be provided for supplying additional oxygen to the engine. This is done by an air pump, called a supercharger, which gathers in air and compresses it, then delivers it to the carburetor for mixture with the gasoline. Suppose that a cubic foot of air at sea level contains one cubic inch of oxygen, and at 20,000 feet contains only 1/3 cubic inch of oxygen. The supercharger must gather in three cubic feet at this altitude, and compress it to one cubic foot, which will then have the proper amount of oxygen. These instruments are regulated so as to compress the air at different altitudes in accordance with the needs of the engine, so there will be a constant supply of air of the same oxygen content as at sea level.

Another internal combustion engine that is receiving a great deal of attention is that known as the Diesel engine. This also was invented by a German, Diesel, in 1877. His interest had been attracted by explosions of dust in grain elevators and other places where a compound of dust was confined and subjected to pressure. On his first experimental engine models, he used coal dust which he sprayed into the cylinders, subjecting them to high compression and obtaining a high order of explosion. Later he used crude oil, from which he obtained even better results.

The flight of Diesel powered airplanes in the United States and Germany in 1928 and 1929 has proved beyond a doubt that the Diesel engine will play a great part in future aircraft power plants. With a given weight of engine and fuel, much longer trips can be made with the Diesel, anywhere from twenty to thirty percent more distance with the present development. If a gasoline engine is able to carry an airplane 3000 miles, a Diesel powered airplane could go almost 4000. The cost of operation is about one-third, as fuel oil such as is burned in ordinary oil furnaces may be used. This costs from 6¢ to 9¢ a gallon, while high test gasoline suitable for airplanes costs from 15¢ to 25¢.

The number of parts in a Diesel engine is much less than in a gasoline engine. The Packard engine which I have recently inspected has 464 parts, whereas the average aircraft gasoline engine has from 2500 to 5000. This simplicity is brought about by several factors, one being that the Diesel engine requires no electrical ignition system which accounts for about one thousand parts. Neither does it require a carburetor, with intake and exhaust manifolds. It requires only one valve in each cylin-

A Supercharged Engine Installation on a Modern Bomber

Packard Diesel Aircraft Engine

der, consequently fewer cams, push rods and timing devices are necessary.

The essential difference in the operation of a Diesel engine as compared to a gasoline engine is that in the latter, the air and fuel are mixed outside the cylinder and then injected into it. This constitutes an explosive mixture before it gets into the cylinder. If for any reason the gasoline engine backfires and the fire reaches this explosive mixture, an explosion with attendant combustion results. With the Diesel engine there can be no backfire because there is nothing to explode on the outside. Combustion is complete inside the cylinder of the Diesel engine, whereas in the gasoline engine it is almost never complete. For instance, at night one may see fire coming out of the exhaust continually.

The operation of the Diesel engine of four-cycle or four-stroke is as follows: On the first down stroke of the piston, the air is sucked into the cylinder. On the second stroke, this is compressed to about 500 pounds to the square inch, developing a temperature of 1000 degrees. Toward the end of the stroke, fuel oil is injected into the cylinder by a pump. On the next stroke, which is the power stroke, the mixture of air and oil explodes and drives the piston down, and on the fourth stroke, the valve is opened and the materials remaining in the cylinder are thrown out through the same valve by which the air was taken in on the first stroke.

With an engine of this kind, having no carburetor, it makes no difference what attitude it may be in, it can fly upside down just as well as right side up. If lubricating oil becomes mixed with the fuel oil, it makes no difference because combustion will be complete in the cylinder anyway, whereas in the gasoline engine, if oil and gas become mixed, it may be followed by serious results. Where a gasoline engine has to be started and slowly warmed up, a Diesel instantly develops its full power, because it does not depend on certain temperatures for carburetion but is dependent on pressure to generate heat for the explosion.

Heavy rain has no effect on the operation of a Diesel engine. It may be covered with water and still carry on; but with the gasoline engine, if any water is taken into the gasoline line, the air intake or the carburetor itself, the engine may be immediately stopped.

As the pressure, or compression as it is usually called, is more than twice that of the ordinary gasoline engine, a different form of starter has to be used. An electric starter could be employed but it would have to be so powerful that its weight would preclude its use in airplanes. This probably could be overcome by having a means of opening the valves on all the cylinders except one, until the engine was started. Inertia starters have been used very successfully, in which a fly wheel is spun up to 20,000 revolutions and this power transmitted through gears to the shaft of the engine. Also there is a starter which utilizes a 12-gauge shotgun cartridge. This arrangement consists of a mechanism like a little gun put in the side of one of the cylinders. The engine is turned until the piston is in a suitable position in this cylinder, when the cartridge is fired, causing the engine to turn and compression to be made in another cylinder and the engine started.

The weight of the Packard aircraft Diesel engine, dry, is about three pounds per horsepower or less, which compares favorably with the gasoline engine. Recently the Packard engine flew for seven hours in a cross country trip from Detroit, Michigan, to Langley Field, Virginia, a distance of about 600 miles. The cost of the fuel used was $4.35. Had it been a gasoline engine, the cost would have been about $30.00.

Aircraft Diesel engines are being experimented with in all countries with varying degrees of success. Some utilize the two cycle or two stroke principle. Some engines are radial and air cooled, others have the cylinders in line and are liquid cooled. The Junkers German Diesel aircraft engine which has flown successfully, has double opposed cylinders, making the engine flat so it will fit right into the leading edge of the wing of an airplane. It is liquid cooled and generates 600 horsepower. It seems probable that for large planes which cover long distances and carry heavy loads, such as bombers in military aviation, and cargo carriers in commercial use, the Diesel engine will in a few years be the most efficient means of motive power we have yet employed.

The cost of the Diesel in production will probably be no more or not even as much as that of the gasoline engine, despite the element of expense incident to constructing its immensely strong cylinders which must withstand great pressures. The tendency in Diesel engine construction is constantly to reduce the pressures in the cylinder, whereas with the gasoline engine the tendency has been to increase the cylinder pressures as new fuels and means of handling them are perfected. It is not impossible that in the future these pressures may become almost the same.

Summing up the advantages of the Diesel engine, one of the most outstanding is the simplicity of operation. The pilot has only one lever or throt-

ENGINES

tle to manipulate, as contrasted to the fuel throttle, air adjustment and spark control on the gasoline engine. With its comparatively few parts, there are not as many sources for trouble to develop. The fire hazard is very much cut down, not only in the airplane itself while in flight, but also on the ground. A lighted match can be thrust into heavy oil and it will not burn. If a piece of cloth is dropped into the oil and the end ignited, it will burn like a wick but the rest of the oil will not burn. A fire of this kind can actually be put out by pouring more fuel oil on it. The fuel tank of the Diesel may be filled while the motor is running, with no danger. One may smoke or throw lighted matches about; consequently insurance rates will be considerably less. The fuel consumption of the Diesel is from twenty to thirty percent less than the gasoline engine, and the cost of operation about seventy percent less. In the absence of an electric ignition system, there is no interference with the radio telegraph and telephone while the airplane is in flight. In the gasoline engine, whenever a spark is made in a spark plug, it starts up radio waves which are received by the wireless instruments, unless all leads going to the spark plugs, or the plugs themselves, are shielded by metal covers.

While the gasoline engine has been brought to a

very high state of perfection and will still be used in great numbers, there is no doubt but that within a few years the Diesel engine will replace it on heavy planes, very much as the Diesel marine motor is supplanting the steam engine on cargo carrying seacraft.

The old steam engine is still very interesting. The cylinders and intake and exhaust valves and the means of connecting these sources of power with the propellor or wheels is simpler and lighter in the steam engine than in any other. But the steam engine depends on heating up a liquid until it becomes gas and then applying this gas to the cylinders. So far we have used gasoline or a similar liquid for heating, but it had to be carried in such quantities that it almost equalled the amount carried by an internal combustion engine for fuel. This was of course in addition to the weight of the water carried. After the water came out of the engines in the form of steam it was nearly all lost, as it is very difficult to recondense steam; so a great deal of water had to be taken along. These difficulties made an efficient aeronautical steam engine impossible. If some liquid could be found that would transform into a gas and then recondense easily, the steam engine might become a competitor of the internal combustion engine. Mercury

ENGINES

has been tried with very interesting results. It turns into a gas easily and can be recondensed much more easily than water. An attempt has been made to construct a mercury vapor turbine. If a turbine engine could be made for an airplane, the working parts would be reduced from the thousands to a few hundred and the simplicity and economy would be tremendous. The power could be directly applied in a rotary manner to the propellor. So far, nothing along this line has been perfected. It has been impossible to make a gasoline or oil turbine engine because the explosions of the fuel could not be applied progressively.

A good deal of experimentation has been done, particularly by Franz Von Opel, on an engine depending on the rocket principle. At one time rockets were used extensively in military operations for projecting missiles, but within the last hundred years they have fallen into desuetude. All engines used for propulsion must transmit their energy in some way. An automobile engine transmits its power to wheels which push against the ground and impel the automobile forward. The energy from an airplane motor is transmitted to the propellor which pushes against the air. The principle of the rocket motor is that a gas is shot out from behind in sufficient quantities and with such force and rapidity that the vehicle is propelled forward in smooth swift flight. Near the earth, of course, this gas presses against the air; but it has been figured out that such a motor could be operated through space, one discharge of gas pressing against the preceding one, so that a machine of this kind would act as long as it could produce sufficient gas against which to push.

There are many other means of transmitting power which are in a theoretical or inventive state. One that promises well for the future is the transmission of electrical power without wires, we might say by radio. Our radio telegraph and telephone are examples of this kind of power transmission. Electric lights can be illuminated by wireless, engines may be run, in fact practically anything may be accomplished by wireless transmission of power that can be done by transmitting electrical power along wires. However it is not economical, as such a tremendous amount of power has to be used. It cannot be confined to a ray or beam but is transmitted in nearly all directions at once. Means for directing these electric currents are constantly being improved and we may look forward to the time when aircraft will be flying through the air equipped with motors whose power is sent them from the ground. Not only will they be furnished

ENGINES

with power but they will be directed along their course and kept in the air electrically. For instance, if a wire were laid from New York to San Francisco which sent out power, airplanes could fly straight along it. If they went to the right or left of the course, the diminished power would act on an instrument to bring them back over the wire. Experiments are being made along this line in many countries. Sources of energy for propelling airplanes are still in their infancy. However, since the invention of the internal combustion engine, there has been no new principle developed which has given us better motive power.

The propellor is one of the airplane's weakest features, from a standpoint of efficiency. A propellor's function is to grab hold of the air and push it behind the airplane. It is evident that a large, broad propellor will take hold of much more air than a small narrow one; yet we see many more small ones in use. This is because the revolutions of the engines have been increased continually, in order to get high horsepower rating. In the old days, propellors and engines turned over about 800 or 900 revolutions, but now they turn over two or three thousand. Engines acting at that high rate of speed are unable to turn a big propellor, therefore smaller ones have to be used. The smaller ones have much more "slip" through the air, which results in a greater loss of tractive power. This has been overcome to some extent by putting gears between the engine and propellor so that the engine may be running at 2000 revolutions, while the propellor is only turning over at 1000. From 700 to 1000 revolutions is the most efficient speed for a propellor.

Not much was known as to the scientific construction of propellors until the airplane began to be used. It is said that the idea for the first water propellor was obtained from watching an oar being used as a scull in the water. The propellor was two, three or four sculls made to go around in a circle. Although airplane propellors are governed by the same principles as those used on sea craft, the first ones were constructed by somewhat empirical methods, the "cut and try" system. If one shape did not give good results, it would be taken off and changed and the experiments continued until one was evolved that worked well. Now it is quite thoroughly understood just what type of propellor will function best with a certain sized airplane.

The "pitch" of the propellor corresponds to the space that the propellor will pull the airplane through in one complete revolution. The airplane might be compared to a screw boring its way through the air. If we put a screw into a piece of

ENGINES

wood and turn it around once, making a complete revolution, the distance it went into the wood might be said to be its "pitch." The pitch of the propellor has to be varied in accordance with whether we want great climbing power or great speed. Often it is a great advantage to be able to vary this pitch while flying, as a change in temperature will make the air lighter or heavier, consequently easier or more difficult for the propellor to take hold of. Propellors are now being made whose pitch may be varied, so that full advantage may be taken of any circumstances, for instance if an airplane has to be climbed very abruptly in getting out of a small field.

Propellors are also made that can be reversed and actually push the airplane backward through the air.

A great many different materials have been used in propellor construction. Naturally the first thing to be used was wood, but it was found this became chewed up easily by rain, sleet or snow; so metal sheathing was used on wood, and later they were made entirely of metal. The ends of a propellor move so fast, up to 400 miles an hour, that when a raindrop hits it, the effect is almost the same as if it were a piece of steel. Metal propellors are able to bore their way through practically any climatic conditions, snow, sleet or rain.

SKYWAYS

While a great deal of development has taken place with propellors, more lies in the future and study and experience of this most important part of aircraft will bring added efficiency in our future flying machines.

CHAPTER III

LEARNING TO FLY

THERE have been very few undertakings of man which have required individual initiative or ability to anywhere near the extent that flying an airplane does. While the principles of flying are comparatively simple, their execution is quite a different matter. The great difference between the pilot in an airplane and the man handling a boat, a horse or a motor car, is the utter aloneness which piloting an airplane entails. When a person goes out for his solo hop, there is no one there to lend advice or encouragement by his voice, or to help with his hands and correct a mistake.

All who wish to fly must first learn to take the airplane off the ground and bring it down again. When we see an airplane resting on the ground with its wheels and tail skid touching the earth, its body inclined upward at an angle of 20 or 30 degrees and the motor still, it hardly ever occurs to us that when we land the plane, we should put it on the ground in just the same position in which we see it resting.

When a student first steps into an airplane, he is taught the manner of handling the controls, which is quite simple. With the universal control now adopted, the rudder is handled by a bar on which the feet are placed. By pressing the right foot, the airplane is turned to the right, and by pressing the left foot, to the left. The stick which comes up between the legs is attached to the elevator. Push forward on it and the nose of the airplane is depressed and you go down. Pull back and the nose is elevated, and you go up. This same stick controls the ailerons, which incline the wings up or down. If the stick is pushed to the right, the right wing goes down. Push to the left and it inclines the left wing downward. Both elevator and wings can be manipulated at the same time by the stick. The way this is done has to be learned by actual practice, it cannot be learned from books or in an artificial way. A long period is required before students become expert in handling it under all conditions.

At first, the student is taught how to maneuver the airplane on the ground. Some systems of instruction make the pupil teach himself. He is furnished with an airplane with very small wings that can not lift itself from the ground, and allowed to taxi all over the airdrome. These machines are called "penguins" because their wings are so small they can not fly, however they have every other

A Mechanical Device for Teaching a Pilot How to Use the Controls

attribute of an airplane. It is almost as difficult to handle an airplane on the ground as it is in the air, especially if the plane is "tricky" in its movements.

The student is shown every position that the airplane should assume when taking off or when landing. It is very important that the airplane be given all the speed possible as it leaves the ground and put exactly in line of flight with its maximum speed before beginning to climb it. A great proportion of the stalls that occur on leaving the ground are caused from climbing the airplane too quickly and at too great an angle. Speed is the thing that an airman always desires, because with it he has control of his machine. But also, speed is the element to which it is difficult for a man to become accustomed. It is harder to handle a horse or an automobile at very high speed than when they are going slowly. Much the same conditions obtain when the airplane is near the ground. That is where most of the trouble occurs.

After the student learns how to "get his tail up," which is the position the airplane must assume in flight, he is given an airplane with slightly larger wings, that can make little hops of 100 feet or so and then settle down again. When he attains proficiency in piloting this type, he is given a machine that can really fly, and to finish him off, he is put into an airplane with two seats, in one of which is an instructor who teaches him the fine points of the flyer's art. The French use this system and it must be said that it produces excellent pilots.

Flying is really an art, as distinguished from a science, and the individual has every chance to show his excellence much in the same way that a fine horseman does in handling his mount. Of all the skilful pilots I have had under my command, probably the best were those who excelled in horsemanship and in the handling of automobiles.

In the United States, most students are started out with an instructor who takes his place in the back seat of the airplane with the student in front of him. First he is shown what the airplane looks like when it is resting on the ground. Then the tail is held up to show the position the airplane takes when it is flying. Then flights are made to give the student the feel of the air and accustom him to the speed necessary to maintain the airplane in flight.

One of the most difficult things about flying instruction is to teach the student when to bring his airplane parallel to the ground preparatory to a landing. On approaching the landing field, the airplane is headed into the wind and glided at a slow safe speed, usually with the engine throttled down to a small number of revolutions. When within thirty or forty feet of the ground, the airplane is gradually pulled up so that its glide becomes more and more parallel to the ground. When the wheels are about four feet from the ground, the airplane is held in that position until it begins to lose flying speed and sink toward the ground. At that instant, the elevator is pulled back to depress the tail and cause the airplane to touch the ground on both wheels and tailskid at the same time. This is what is called a "three-point landing" and puts the airplane back on the ground in the same position as when the pilot first got into it.

The pilot must learn to take advantage of all air currents. When actually up in the air, the method of handling the airplane is no different, no matter how the wind blows. It is immersed in a fluid that is just the same all around, and it makes no difference if it is passing over the earth at a rate of 10 or 100 miles an hour, or is making no headway at all. But when the pilot gets near the ground, it makes a great difference if he is going with or against a wind. Suppose that he is going with a wind of 60 miles an hour and his stalling speed is 60 miles, the minimum speed he can hope to maintain would amount to 120 miles an hour, that is, the airplane's speed plus the speed of the wind. This is much too great a speed at which to hit the ground. The danger in landing is proportional to the speed one is going. If on the other hand this airplane with a slow speed of 60 miles flies against a wind blowing 60 miles an hour, a capable pilot can land his airplane with no ground speed at all, the wheels and tailskid touching at the same time and resting there without rolling forward. The greatest difficulty that any flying man encounters is judging between what is safe flying speed and what is stalling speed, or the minimum speed at which the plane can be flown with all the controls acting with rapidity and certainty.

When I made my first solo flights, I had little idea of regulating the speed of my plane when I came near the ground. Being fearful of losing flying speed, I allowed the machine to go too fast. Fortunately I made a few successful landings at high speed because I happened to bring the airplane in at an angle that was parallel to the ground. My instructor kept telling me to get my tail down but he did not tell me I was landing too fast, consequently in the next landing I attempted, when I touched the ground I pulled back on my elevator suddenly and the airplane had so much speed that it shot up about thirty feet, where it stalled, fell off on one wing, crashed and turned over. This

LEARNING TO FLY
taught me more about landings than anything that has ever occurred, before or since.

When the airplane first starts to stall, one usually experiences a sinking feeling. Some men are not able to feel this sensation, and most frequently they are the ones who are killed early in their flying experience. First the ailerons on the end of the wings fail to function; one can push the stick from one side to the other and there is no response. When an experienced pilot feels this, he pushes the nose of his ship down and gets more speed. After the ailerons cease working, unless speed is immediately regained, the elevator becomes useless, then the rudder. About that time the airplane begins to fall off on a wing and go into a spin. When an airplane has reached that point, nothing can save it except a fall of about 300 feet, in order to pick up the necessary speed.

In the old days some airplanes had very large control surfaces, especially elevator and rudder, and so little was known about stalls that a pilot, when he got into one, would attempt to pull his plane out instead of first allowing it to gain sufficient speed by falling, with the result that he held his plane in a stall all the way to the ground and crashed fatally. This was especially the case in one of the early Wright machines, called the "B-

Wright." Lieut. Milling, one of the great pioneer flyers of the United States, was flying one of these B-Wrights at the time the accidents were happening. From his study of the accidents, he concluded that the pilots in trying to bring their planes out of a stall pulled back on their elevators, which were so strong that they kept the ship in a stall all the way down. He reasoned that if the plane were allowed to fall with the controls held in a neutral position, it would pick up speed of its own accord and could soon be handled again. It took great courage to demonstrate this, but he purposely stalled one of these planes, allowing it to fall and then regaining control. This is the first instance of a voluntary stall in the air that we know of. His conclusions, of course, were correct and this one accomplishment saved the lives of many people.

A good flying instructor will put his student into every kind of position imaginable. He will shut off the engine, making him land in difficult places with no engine, a "dead-stick landing" as it is called. In teaching acrobatics, the instructor will cut the engine unexpectedly, so the student will become used to regaining control of the airplane under all circumstances. This is a valuable part of his training and later when flying his own plane he will not lose his head no matter under what trying conditions he may find himself.

It has interested me to note the change in the psychological attitude of the student pilot, which has come about in the last few years. In the old days, the feat of flying was so strange and new that it was with the greatest difficulty that the student was enabled to overcome his feeling of trepidation, of being out of place in the air. Even when he learned to fly, he was never completely at home in the air, but always thought of things in relation to the ground or water. Now things are quite different, and a flyer thinks of his plane as a part of himself. Today men know airplanes, just as their fathers knew motor cars and as their grandfathers knew horses and carriages. They have read about them, talked about them and really felt the air before they ever went into it.

Some men are never able to fly, on account of temperamental unfitness, nervousness, lack of moral stability or some physical defect. Some who learn to fly quickly never make excellent pilots, and others who learn slowly make the finest types. Some men are able to find their way across country with great ease, reading their maps correctly and always arriving at their destination. Other excellent pilots are continually getting lost. In these days of marked airways across country, where the pilot is led by easily distinguished marks or beacon lights at night, flying across country is as easy as walking down a lighted street.

During the first part of the war in Europe, many of my pilots on the front would get lost, sometimes landing in German territory. They had maps mounted on cases with rollers in them so they could move the map as they progressed in any direction, but they would get lost just the same. I suspected that they looked at the maps too much instead of at the ground, so I had the maps pasted on the lower wings of the airplane. Still they lost their way; so I took the maps away from them entirely and then practically none were lost because they watched the landmarks.

Above all, a pilot must use his eyes. He must be able to judge distances and speed. When he brings his airplane toward the ground, he must estimate correctly the distance to the earth and adjust his speed accordingly. Once when I was making a forced landing in mountains, due to a heavy storm, I signalled my aide who was flying another plane, to watch where I landed and then to do the same thing. There were a great many undulations in the ground and I had to go over one small hill while I still had flying speed, keep flying until I got to a little stream beyond it and then land uphill on the other side. My aide, instead of doing as I had done, levelled off over this piece of ground just as though it had been a flat flying field, with the result that he stalled beyond the crest of the first hill, and smashed his airplane all to pieces in the bottom of the little stream. .Although this man was a distinguished flyer with many years' experience, he did not use his eyes to good advantage, failing to size up his distances and maintain proper speed. He was killed about a year later, largely for this same reason. A pilot must be able to see in front of him, behind him, sideways and up and down. He must know at just what instant he can put his tail down for a landing. The ability to land at minimum speed is what saves lives. If a man can do this, his life and the lives of the people with him will not be lost, no matter if he has to land in forests, mountains, water or in the streets of a city.

Flying itself is the basis of all aeronautical education, although about 70 trades and professions contribute toward the makeup and construction of an airplane. The highly developed aeronautical expert must not only have great vision for the future but must be a scientist and well versed in mathematics, mechanics, civil, mechanical and electrical engineering, aero-dynamics, chemistry, knowledge of metals, materials, strains and stresses on structures; navigation, both celestial and by the aid of radio; business and industrial organization and administration. The military airman, in addition to these things, has to be familiar with the operation and control of armies and navies; with civil, military and admiralty laws as applied to air traffic; with the systems of communications of countries, such as roads, railroads, canals and steamship lines, also where food supplies and provisions are obtained, the location of the great cities and vital points of the country, so that in case of war he will know where and how to attack.

For these reasons, the education of the highest type airman embraces more subjects and more thorough knowledge of world conditions than has ever been required of one person or profession.

CHAPTER IV

THE KIND OF MEN TO MAKE INTO PILOTS

MOST healthy young men or women from 16 to 40 years of age can be taught to fly an ordinary airplane. A great majority of these may become very good pilots for transport or passenger carrying machines in time of peace; but the requirements for a military aviator call for more concentrated physical and mental ability in the individual than has ever been necessary in any calling heretofore.

The military flyer must move at tremendous speed through the air. Not only must he fly his own airplane, but he must see all the other airplanes around him, friendly as well as hostile ones; he must observe the ground, be ready to attack or defend himself at any instant, be ready to land on any sort of surface, mountains, forests, plowed ground. He may have to fly for hundreds or thousands of miles to his destination and there deliver his cargo or bombs, or report what he sees, or make his attack either against hostile air forces, vessels on the sea or vital centers. It is a supreme test of character and courage. Often no one is watching. If he shows the white feather or is inclined to "beat" what he is instructed to do, often no one can be the wiser.

When he returns he may tell a fantastic tale about things that never occurred without much danger of being checked up.

I have seen this done in many instances. On one notable occasion, the pilot shot all his ammunition away into the empty air and returned to report that he was out of ammunition. This resulted in the death of one of our greatest aviators because he was left without assistance and had to close with the enemy alone. In other cases, I have known men who were excellent pilots behind the lines but the instant they came into the presence of the enemy, either their machine guns jammed or they would have engine trouble or something that required their leaving that vicinity immediately. They would land with a plausible story which was impossible to disprove. Other men were perfectly free in their admission that when they came into the presence of the enemy, they were absolutely unable to control themselves. These men were brave, resourceful and patriotic but they did not have the moral qualities required for that kind of work.

With an army on the ground, a person is shoulder to shoulder with another. If he is wounded, he can lie down on the ground and be aided by his comrades. If he is on the sea, he is in a ship close to his companions. When in the air, however, he is away from these, off by himself thousands of feet up. If he is not successful, he goes down in flames. These things are not so pleasant to talk about, but they are the things that affect a man's mind.

The American makes a particularly good pilot because he comes of sturdy stock, with the pioneering instinct of doing something new still in him. He is brought up in our schools and universities to play games that require a good deal of courage, particularly American football. The other games, such as baseball, basket ball, hockey and tennis, not only teach him individual initiative and self-reliance but to rely on his comrades, to work together in a team and to acquire the kind of discipline necessary in the air. This is "thinking discipline" in which the individual estimates exactly what his orders mean and then carries them out by using his head in accordance with the circumstances that exist.

The old discipline, as conceived and carried out by armies and navies throughout the centuries, consists in the unhesitating obedience by a subordinate to the orders of his superior. In that case the subordinate is not supposed to think too much. If he does, he may "spill the beans" and tie up the whole operation. This kind of discipline has been designed for the average man. It is only within the last generation that most of the men composing armies could read or write. The development of their mentality on the average was of a comparatively low order. With the aviator, however, the keenest, best educated, most advanced type of man has to be selected. These are some of the reasons why an officer raised in an army or navy atmosphere is totally incapable of understanding an airplane pilot's mentality or the way to handle or develop him.

The development of aviation and its undoubted assumption of the principal means of national defense in which a comparatively small number of individuals will do the work, will result in a condition similar to that during the Middle Ages when the fighting was done by a few knights in armor while the rest of the people supported them. Today the nation that has suitable men to make into aviators and the industrial background and resources to create airplanes and equipment will certainly dominate the future world. Like everything else, the execution will depend on the individual.

Physically, the doctors tell us a great deal about how the man should be constituted. A great many of their deductions are correct. They say he must be sound in the eyes, in the heart and lungs. His inner ear must be capable of determining balance. He must be free from disease, must have good hands and feet, legs, arms and body, and probably hair on his head. But some of the greatest aviators we have ever had have been afflicted with tuberculosis, have had only one eye, have had a club foot, have had bad hearts and been otherwise impaired.

We hear a great deal about the age at which people have to begin or stop flying. This also is relative. I have seen men begin to fly in their late thirties who became extraordinary pilots. Naturally, when a man gets over forty his eyes begin to lose the power of accommodation, but this only means that they are unable to focus quickly on near objects at ordinary reading distances, that is, twenty inches from the eyes. A man who has sound eyes at any age can see perfectly well for flying. Of course if his eyes have astigmatism, he is always burdened with them. I know some men whose vision was astigmatic, who memorized the eye tests and "got by" with them, and made excellent pilots. On the other hand, there were other men who did the same thing and it was directly responsible for their death. My own brother met his death in an airplane for that reason.

It was interesting to see how pilots were trained by the different countries during the war to get the most out of them. One country did not teach its pilots what the dangers were. It took them when they were very young and consequently inexperienced, and instilled into them the idea of closing with the enemy and destroying him, irrespective of loss. Their theory was that men taught in this way, no matter if they did incur greater losses, would destroy a great many of the enemy. If their side had a greater number of pilots, they would win in the end; but it did not work out that way.

Another nation taught its pilots to be too cautious, and enlarged too much on the dangers of air work, consequently they did not do as much as they should. I have always tried to teach our pilots every side of the question and then to have them push forward to the accomplishment of their tasks with a thorough knowledge of everything that lay in front of them.

A study of medicine as applied to men engaged in aviation has helped very greatly, not only in the selection of men suitable to become pilots, but in the handling of these men while flying. In order to fully understand conditions, the doctor should be a flyer himself. Some of our best medical men have been excellent pilots. The good ones could look at a pilot as he walked past and tell what condition he was in, mentally, physically and morally. I have sometimes watched doctors in the Marine Hospital service examining immigrants and as these people walked through a narrow aperture one by one, the doctors could tell by the way they looked, walked or glanced around whether there was any inherent trouble in them, even obscure diseases of the internal organs. In the same way a flight surgeon is able to tell with almost unerring accuracy whether a man is in suitable shape to keep on with his flying.

Shortly after the war I had a comparatively large air force assembled at Langley Field, Virginia, which was being used in a test to demonstrate how battleships could be sunk by air bombs. The operation was conducted far out over the Atlantic and was one of the most difficult and dangerous we had ever been called upon to perform. Major Strong, my flight surgeon, was a man of great ability and experience. Every man was inspected and looked after before he got into his ship. They did not know this was being done but the doctors were on hand everywhere. We lost no pilots at sea during the operation and I think that the doctors were as much responsible for these results as were the excellent mechanics who kept the motors in condition, or the thorough air instruction and discipline maintained.

Like all other branches of medicine, aviation medicine has become a very complicated and technical subject, in fact a little too much so, I think. A careful selection of the persons who are to become pilots, however, is an extremely necessary thing.

When the student flyer presents himself for medical examination, his whole physical history is investigated, particularly the stability of his nervous system. Inquiries are even made as to the diseases from which his mother and father may have died, so as to determine, for instance, if any rheumatism has been present, which may have a direct action on diseases of the heart. Recent attacks of malarial fever will be renewed if a man flies at high altitude where it is cold. Hay fever is carefully looked into, because it may be something else. Asthma, which causes a restriction of breathing, is serious.

Various altitude tests are applied to find out his "ceiling," or how high he can go before he must be supplied artificially with additional oxygen.

The eye is a tremendously important organ in an aviator's makeup and a man's vision is tested by many different kinds of apparatus to determine not only the power of sight at various distances but how quickly the eye can change and adapt itself from seeing nearby objects to those at some distance.

The sense of balance resides in the inner ear, and the drums of the ear and Eustachian tubes must be in good condition. As the aviator changes altitude rapidly, the two sides of his ear drums are exposed to unequal pressure which may break the ear drum. From this he may have severe headache, deafness, dizziness or may even become unconscious.

A pilot must take plenty of exercise which will make for a quick coordination of mind and muscle. Any vigorous outdoor exercise is good, particularly horseback riding, playing tennis or handball.

Staleness and fatigue must be watched for carefully. If a man becomes tired, his reflexes and senses do not work rapidly and this may result in serious accidents. It can be readily told when a pilot is approaching staleness and when he does, he should be given relaxation and his mind taken up with other matters than flying. A man may become so stale and tired out that it will affect his mind and make him totally unfit ever to fly again.

Breeding and environment have a great deal to do with the individual making a good pilot or a poor one. Just as the Anglo-Saxons and Scandinavians made the best navigators the world has ever seen, so the people of Anglo-Saxon and Norse stock make excellent pilots. While many individuals of other races make good pilots, I doubt if any others, as a race, have the stamina, quick perception and initiative in the air which the Anglo-Saxons possess.

CHAPTER V

WEATHER

WEATHER is a most important consideration for the flying man whether he be in an airplane, airship or an ordinary balloon. The air is in a state of constant motion much like the waves and currents of the sea. While sea water is more or less of the same consistency everywhere, the air is subject to very great changes.

There are two phases of the weather which vitally affect the aviator. One has to do with the degree of visibility such as fogs, heavy rains, snow, sleet or clouds. The other is concerned with the air itself, when it is directed hither and thither by heavy winds, storms, squalls or hurricanes. All of these phenomena occur in certain localities and for certain periods. A good weather forecasting system will give notice to the aviator as to where the storms or other hazards are, what areas they cover, how deep they are (that is, how many feet above the ground), and how long they will last.

Heavy fog is a very serious impediment to flying. When in a fog everything looks the same to the flyer. It is just as though he were on the inside of a sphere painted grey all around. He has no horizon to look at, no point of reference on which he may level his plane, and no way of telling whether his airplane is right side up or upside down, except by artificial means. He may stall the ship and fall to earth, or he may fly on his side or even upside down without knowing he is doing so.

Fog areas usually occur when a current of warm air, heavily laden with moisture, meets a current of cool air, which condenses the moisture into fogs and clouds. Such is the case with the fogs over the Atlantic Ocean where the warm air of the Gulf Stream meets the cold air coming down from Greenland, or in the Pacific where the air from the Japanese current meets the cold air coming from Bering Sea and the Aleutian Islands. The fog banks are very dense near the surface of the water, especially in summer. They are not very deep, usually from three to eight hundred feet, which can be flown over easily. In the vicinity of the Great Lakes also there are fog areas, usually not over 200 miles in width.

Wherever it is very cold the atmosphere is not able to hold moisture, and fogs do not occur. In the Arctic and sub-Arctic regions, where the temperature in winter falls to between 30 and 70 degrees below zero, the air can hold very little moisture. Neither fogs nor clouds occur here, nor winds of high velocity, because there is not sufficient heat in the atmosphere to cause up and down currents of air which in their turn produce winds. Consequently flying conditions are very good as far as the air is concerned.

Up to the present time, flying in fog is the most serious problem the flyer has to solve. Scientifically there is nothing particularly difficult about the solution. A gyroscopic instrument called the "automatic pilot" is able to hold the airplane on an even keel, to give it direction and to make turns. But so far no device has been produced, practical under all conditions, which will indicate to the pilot how far above the ground he is, and whether there are any obstructions beneath him such as trees, high buildings, church steeples, electric wires and so on. It is the one great obstacle to what might be called "universal flying," that is, flying all over the world under any conditions.

Rain storms offer no particular impediment to the modern airplane. When wooden propellors were used, the rain chewed them up a good deal. The tip of a propellor moves at a rate of speed between 300 and 400 miles per hour and when rain hits it at such a speed, the effect is like shot fired into a wooden board. With metal propellors, this difficulty is eliminated. In the average rainstorm or snowstorm below the cloud level, visibility is fairly good and the pilot is able to see a sufficient distance ahead and under him to find his way and land when necessary. However, when a snowstorm is mixed with hail or sleet, another serious hazard faces the aviator. The wings and whole structure of the ship will become encrusted with ice, even the propellor. This not only weights the airplane down greatly but changes the shapes of the control surfaces so they will not steer or handle the airplane in the way they should. Without doubt, many of the flyers who attempted to fly the Atlantic have tried to rise up over rain or snowstorms and by doing so have gotten up to the "hail line," the altitude where the water in the atmosphere is frozen, and their ships have become so encrusted with ice as to fall out of control.

Often when water is held in suspension in the air in the form of rain, although the temperature around it is down to freezing, the specific heat of the water keeps these raindrops from becoming ice; but when the wings of an airplane hit them and break the water up into fine particles, it immediately freezes and encrusts the wings and control surfaces with ice. If this does not go too far, it may improve the airplane by causing it to be more streamlined and smoothing out lots of little projecting points which offer resistance to the air; but a limit is soon reached.

I have had many experiences with the formation of ice on planes, one of the worst of which occurred in 1921. I had gone to Ithaca, New York, on an inspection trip, and in flying back to Long Island, I encountered a series of rain clouds. They did not look very high so I decided to fly over them. With a single engined ship this is a good deal of a risk, because if the engine fails a forced landing will have to be made, and the clouds may extend all the way to the ground. I reached the top of the clouds at an altitude of about 12,000 feet and proceeded on my way. Gradually the level of the top of the clouds became higher and higher, until about 16,000 feet had been reached and my airplane could rise no further. I turned around in an attempt to retrace my way, but found that the cloud level had raised behind me and was rising even at the place where I was. In another plane accompanying me was my aide, Lieut. Maitland. I signalled him that we would go down through the clouds, and he therefore went in a direction opposite to mine so as to minimize the possibility of our running into each other. In those days we did not have parachutes and any sort of crash in the air meant sure death.

I knew full well that we were above the hail line

WEATHER

and that we would encounter hail, snow and sleet in the clouds. As I went into them, everything grew dark. It was almost black inside and I could feel hail and snow hitting me in the face as I looked out. I attempted a gentle glide downward at about 80 miles per hour but my air speed indicator soon began to show a much lower speed. I pushed my airplane forward to increase the speed and soon from the singing of the wind in the wires I could tell I was going faster than 80 miles, probably around 150. It then dawned on me that the Pitot tube into which air was admitted for the air speed indicator had become clogged with snow and ice and was useless. About that time my engine began to vibrate tremendously. The vibrations increased even when I slowed the motor down, until I was afraid the engine would be torn out of its bed. Snow and sleet kept swirling by and I could see it form heavily on wings and wires. I had to put my head out of the cockpit to feel the pressure of air, so as to tell at what speed I was going, and the snow and sleet cut like a knife.

I succeeded in keeping the ship more or less in flying position although sometimes I would fall off on one wing and then another. I kept watching my altimeter as I went down rapidly from 16,000 feet. Gradually the hail turned to snow and the snow to rain. At about 2000 feet the density of the cloud grew distinctly less and at 1500 feet I began to see the ground. I was over on my left wing. I came out directly above Binghamton, New York, and began to give the engine a little more throttle so as to pull myself up straight. My controls were acting in a very slow and dead manner. To my surprise, instead of the motor vibrating worse, it was distinctly better. I could see ice leaving the propellor and in a few minutes the vibrations had ceased. I determined that they had been caused by ice forming on the propellor unevenly, thereby throwing it out of balance. Maitland joined me a few moments later, having had the same experience as mine. When we landed at Mitchel Field, Long Island, we found a tremendous lot of ice all over our ships, including the undercarriages and control surfaces.

Many pilots had encountered similar conditions but up to that time most of them had been killed, so their experiences were never related. Every instrument I had that depended on the air stream for its functioning proved worthless. The altimeter and the ordinary liquid compass were the only things that continued to do their work. I had a gyroscopic turn indicator which depended on an air stream going through a tube to spin the gyroscope, but as this tube clogged up, the instrument became useless. Gyroscopes in an airplane must be actuated by engines in order to insure their efficiency.

The formation of ice on airplanes can be counteracted by heating the wings artificially, or by putting on compounds which will cause the frost and water to slide off them, or which will generate heat when water touches them. Recently a mixture of calcium chloride and certain other chemicals, the formula for which is the creation of a professor at McGill University, Canada, was tried and found practical to melt snow and ice on city streets. It is said to have melted the ice around a ship frozen in, so that it was able to get to open water. A compound such as this applied to the wings of an airplane would undoubtedly keep the ice off. Coatings of paraffin have also been tried with partial success.

An electric or thunder storm accompanied by high winds is a dangerous thing to fly into. Although lightning has seldom hit a plane, I remember one instance where the wings of a plane were perforated by lightning and neither of the two occupants were hurt in the least. The worst thunderstorms I ever encountered were in the vicinity of Chesapeake Bay, in the summer. The sun gives out a great deal of heat in the morning which warms the air, and draws water up into it from the Bay or ocean. This current of rising air pushes out all around, as it is expanded. Gradually it reaches out toward the Blue Ridge and the Allegheny Mountains which are covered with trees. The leaves of trees are among the greatest absorbers of heat we know. By the time the hot moisture laden air arrives at these hills, it is afternoon, and the sun is beginning to decline and lose some of its heat. That, combined with the cool air from the mountains, causes the moisture to condense and clouds to form. The cold air begins pouring down the sides of the mountains back toward the Bay. Storms begin forming "against the wind." Gradually the storm clouds, or thunder heads as they are called, assume very great proportions. Clouds rise as high as the atmosphere will hold moisture, which is thought to be about 55,000 feet. As the clouds progress, static electricity begins to form in them and they act like the plates of an electrical condenser, the clouds being one part of it and the earth the other. The electric tension becomes so great that lightning occurs. By this time the storm is well on its way to being a serious menace to aviators and to ships on the water. These storms are usually about 20 or 30 miles in diameter and they move from one place to another at the rate of about twenty miles per hour; but inside them the wind is whipping around in all sorts of ways, and velocities up to 125 miles per hour have been recorded. Ordinarily an airplane can fly around these storms.

Once I started out from Langley Field, Virginia, with eight airplanes following me. We ran into a series of these great thunderstorms. All the airplanes except one were forced down. One of them, containing eight people, crashed and everyone was killed.

A modern airplane equipped with a good gyroscopic pilot can go straight through these storms with impunity; but with the ordinary plane that is being built, storms such as this are almost sure to cause disaster. The air within these storms is in a great state of agitation. There are up currents, down currents and lateral currents as the electrical conditions and moisture conditions in the clouds change so rapidly. Where the air touches the ground, it is retarded just as the lower part of a stream of water is slowed up by obstructions on the stream bed. Compared to water, the air moves very rapidly, so the upper air tumbles over the air close to the ground resulting in a condition like a cylinder of air rolling along. The old low-powered airplanes were unable to pull up through these currents, being driven to the ground by the sheer force of the air.

Where several thunderstorms run together and

form a line, what is known as a "line squall" is the result. On one side of this line squall there will be a current of rising air and on the other, a current of falling air. It acts very much like a waterfall going in two ways, one down and the other up. The dirigible airship, on account of its length, is fearful of these line squalls. The United States airship Shenandoah was caught in one and torn apart in the middle. Modern dirigibles are being built very thick and strong in the middle, so as to resist such pressures.

The "bumps" that we feel when flying in the air are the result of up or down currents. The heavy cumulus clouds we see on a warm day are always the upper ends of strong up-currents of air, while the clear spaces between them, especially over mountains covered with trees, have down-currents. The old spherical balloonists knew these conditions even better than the airplane pilot because they were entirely dependent on the way the air took them. What are known as "holes in the air" are really down currents. There can be no such thing as a hole in the air.

As the sun loses its force in the evening, the heat reflected from the earth diminishes. The winds die down and usually by about midnight a calm begins to creep over the darkened earth. By two o'clock

WEATHER

in the morning conditions are usually very quiet and from that time until sunrise the best atmospheric conditions obtain for flying. It is then that most of the migratory birds make their flights. They know this is the best time, from long experience. The inner ear of birds is so sensitive that it corresponds to the barometers that we use and they can tell a day ahead of time by the pressure in their ears if storms or high winds are coming.

Those who use the radio know that in the hours between two o'clock in the morning and daylight there is less static than at any other time. This is because there are fewer thunderstorms and less heavy cloud formations carrying charges of electricity, and less light ions pervading our atmosphere than at any other time. Light is practically the same thing as electricity and the undulation which we recognize in our radio is merely a long wave length of light off the red end of the spectrum, which we could see if our eyes were a little different. It is probably a good thing that our eyes are as they are, otherwise we would see all sorts of things going through the air.

The shape of the earth actuates certain currents of air. If the wind hits against a cliff or side of a mountain, an up current will be produced. If it blows against a cliff, the back of which has a vertical face a few hundred feet in height, there will be wind eddies from the sides or from the top very much the way there are water eddies around a rock in a stream. This sometimes results disastrously to airplanes of low power. I have seen airplanes flying behind very large ships fall into the sea in going into one of these air eddies.

A straight head wind is no particular impediment to the flyer except that it slows up his speed. In flying against a wind, it is usually better for an airplane to get down as low as possible to the ground. Not only is the least wind encountered here, but as the airplane pushes the air in front of it and under it, it is constantly flying over a cushion of air. If the plane is flying close to water, say within ten or fifteen feet of it, the bottom of this air cushion strikes the water with the result that the airplane gets considerable more sustentation and its speed consequently is increased. When flying far out to sea, I have often run into winds forty or fifty miles an hour in velocity close to the water but 100 or 150 miles an hour a few thousand feet up. Over the water, I had nothing to gain by flying at altitude because if one has engine trouble one must land in the water anyway. So I always got as close to the water as possible, in that way obtaining greater lift, speed and less wind velocity.

WEATHER

It was determined many years ago that the height of the barometric column and its variation foretold to an extent what the weather would be. The column of mercury in the barometer measures approximately the height of the column of air over its position. By noting this from time to time, together with the direction and intensity of the wind and the form and kind of cloud masses, predictions for 24 hours ahead can be made in any one place. If readings of this nature are made over a large area, for instance from one coast of the United States to the other, predictions about the weather could be made from thirty-six to forty-eight hours in advance. If similar readings and weather data were assembled from all over the world, predictions could be made for even longer periods than two days. This is what is called forecasting.

Weather bureaus in all countries give out notices of storms and disturbances which will affect the farmers, fruit growers, those interested in animal industry and those engaged in shipping. They also get out daily weather maps which show the high and low areas of barometric pressure, which show the way the wind is blowing as it pours from a higher to a lower place. The difference in barometric pressure is often indicative of how fast the wind will blow, whether a gale, hurricane or cyclone.

Some almanacs forecast the weather a year or more ahead of time. This is done by comparing statistics about the weather at any given time for a period of forty or fifty years, then comparing these with the state of the moon, sun spots and condition of other celestial bodies. It is remarkable how accurate some of these "Farmer's Weather Almanacs" are. I have often used them in arranging the time at which I would begin certain aeronautical operations and usually found the predictions substantially correct.

There are prevalent many traditions about the weather among farmers and seafaring people who are dependent for their livelihood on being able to judge it. These are often expressed in proverbs or verse such as the following, most of which are good reliable statements as to how the weather will act under certain conditions:

> Red sky in the morning
> Is a sailor's warning.
> Red sky at night
> Sailor's delight.
>
> Evening red and morning gray
> Help the traveler on his way;
> Evening gray and morning red
> Bring down rain upon his head.

WEATHER

A rainbow in the morning
Is the shepherd's warning;
A rainbow at night
Is the shepherd's delight.

The higher the clouds, the finer the weather.

Mackerel scales and mares' tails
Make lofty ships carry low sails.

Whene'er the clouds do weave
'Twill storm before they leave.

Rain long foretold, long last;
Short notice, soon past.

When the morn is dry
The rain is nigh.
When the morn is wet
No rain you get.

A veering wind, fair weather;
A backing wind, foul weather.

Apropos of the last couplet, a veering wind in the northern hemisphere is one that goes around from east to north to west to south, clockwise. A backing wind goes from east to south to west to north. In the northern hemisphere, a backing wind is nearly always indicative of storms whereas a veering wind is the normal and portends fair weather. In the southern hemisphere, the reverse is true.

Flying has given us a knowledge of these things we could have obtained in no other way. It is now believed that there are definite currents in the upper atmosphere, at 25,000 or 30,000 feet, which in the northern hemisphere blow from west to east and in the southern hemisphere blow from east to west, at velocities up to 200 miles an hour. The causes of these phenomena are not yet definitely known but it is thought they are much the same as those which govern the flow of the Japanese current in the Pacific and the Gulf Stream in the Atlantic.

Some years ago experiments were conducted in high altitude flying with the object of finding out more about these currents, and for this purpose a metal cabinet was constructed, which was hermetically sealed and equipped with tanks of oxygen which maintained the same air pressure in the cabin as that at ordinary altitudes. A satisfactory method was evolved for absorbing the gases given out by the breath, and a new system of controls was devised. Ordinary controls, consisting of levers which must be moved through a considerable space, could not be used as they would necessitate holes in the cabin. It was found that by means of electric controls, the rudder, elevators and ailerons could be governed equally well. If a plane with a speed of 300 miles an hour were equipped with such a cabin and entered a 300 mile wind in the upper air, it could attain the appalling speed of 600 miles per hour.

People have always tried either to determine what the weather will be ahead of time or to control it in some way. Efforts have been made to dispel fog and make rain. I authorized experiments to be conducted along these lines for several years which met with considerable success, and gave promise of possible future benefits.

The principle upon which the dispelling of fog is based is that the moisture held in clouds or fog is of a certain electrical polarity, either positive or negative. This can be determined by an electroscope, an instrument which shows what kind of electricity a certain charge is. Then by taking small particles of sand and electrifying them with the opposite polarity and scattering this through the fog or cloud, the particles of water and sand will attract each other, coming together and falling in the form of rain. I have seen avenues cut right through clouds by this method; but it required so much sand and electrical energy that it was not practical.

Some people who followed the experiments became so enthusiastic over the possibilities that they were certain they could go into arid regions over which clouds passed but did not deposit their water, and instead of using particles of sand, they would use grass seed and electrify them. They would fall with the water on these deserts and presently verdure would spring up. In a year or so, green fields would be covered with cattle and sheep, and large populations. They even went so far as to estimate that they might cause floods by this method which could wash away cities, and therefore they would have to be careful in their applications of it. While these things seem like fancies from the realms of romance, they are scientifically possible, and in the future man may be able to control the weather to a great extent.

We know the average width of storms all over the world, the average density and depth of fogs, what the wind velocities are, the directions in which they blow, and our airways should be laid out in accordance with these things. It is perfectly practical to lay out three airways across the United States, and to other continents, some three or four hundred miles apart. If heavy storms were reported along a part of the middle route, for instance, airplanes flying this route could shift to the northern or southern route and continue on their way. A pilot could be kept constantly informed by radio telegraph or telephone of what was happening ahead of him and on a well organized airway he should be informed

WEATHER

every five minutes of what weather he might expect fifty or one hundred miles ahead. Most serious accidents to aircraft occur in storms and a well organized weather service is essential to successful air navigation.

CHAPTER VI

FLYING FIELDS AND AIRWAYS

AIRPLANES have to start from and come back to a flying field, therefore the organization and handling of fields is a very important matter. Although the air is almost limitless in scope, it is remarkable how many collisions may occur in it if energetic measures are not taken for traffic control. Airplanes must be routed along certain airways, in accordance with the time of day and state of the weather. Pilots must be given complete information of what airplanes they are apt to encounter en route. Adequate inspection of their engines and navigating equipment and radio must be provided for ahead of time and they should know when and what to report as they pass over certain stations on the airways.

In commercial aviation, our primary consideration is safety so the flying field or airdrome must be carefully chosen. If it is to handle the air traffic of a city it must be placed as close to the center of population as possible because if it is too far out, an hour or two by automobile, the advantage of greater speed may be obviated, and it may be more convenient to use the railroad or automobile. At Chicago, for instance, there used to be an airdrome

FIELDS AND AIRWAYS

that it took one and a half hours to get to. The distance from Chicago to Milwaukee is about eighty miles and it could be flown in 40 minutes. But one could take a train or automobile and get to Milwaukee in two hours, which was quicker.

Some day airports will be organized on platforms or roofs of buildings. All means of transportation, railroads, steamships and automobiles, will have terminals concentrated in that vicinity so as to give the greatest economy and rapidity in changing from one kind of transport to the other. A passenger on an airplane coming in to New York from San Francisco might want to take a steamship to Europe, so the wharf should be alongside the airdrome. He might want to take a train to Philadelphia or a motor bus to Long Island, and the station should be near at hand. The concentration of population in certain centers requires that as little surface space as possible be devoted to transportation. Already a tremendous congestion of transportation is prevalent in all great cities and we must sooner or later establish different sub-surface levels or stages for the various kinds.

Until our means of flying through and landing in fogs and storms is entirely perfected, the ordinary flying field such as we have known for the last ten years will be in use.

To begin with, a safe place must be provided for landing. The air field should be easy to see and find from the air, and easy to approach. There should be no high buildings in close proximity to it, no radio towers or church steeples, no forests, and above all, no high tension electric power lines or telegraph and telephone wires strung next to it. It is astonishing to see how often an otherwise excellent, well selected flying field is soon covered with hangars, radio poles, flag poles and all sorts of obstructions. This is because the people building up the airport are not flyers themselves and do not know these things. The obstructions above the ground on an airport must be reduced to a minimum.

Another strange thing one observes is that nearly all airports near cities are alongside the cemeteries, probably because cemeteries are usually out in the suburbs and near the only available flying ground. But this does not have a particularly cheering effect on passengers or pilots. On rising or landing, they see the cemetery conveniently near, usually with a funeral taking place.

As to the size and shape of the airport, it should be about one hundred acres in extent, flat, level and well drained, and laid out so that airplanes can take advantage of the prevailing wind. The average

FIELDS AND AIRWAYS

airplane, when fully loaded, requires a run of about 800 feet on the ground to take off and somewhat less than this when landing. This run may be lengthened to about 1200 feet under certain conditions. At first the airplane rises slowly, about one foot for every ten, and gradually pulls up to about one foot in every five. All airplanes when leaving the ground should first be held down until their high speed is obtained so that the pilot will have entire control. They should not be climbed too rapidly as this might cause a stall. This requires that the outer edges of the field be clear of obstructions. A first class airdrome should be at least 2500 feet on a side and rectangular or circular in form.

The surface should not be too hard or too soft. It should not be dusty, so very light soil should be avoided. It should be well drained and not subject to floods. What tears the airdromes to pieces usually is sharp tail skids on airplanes. Tail skids should be prohibited and wheels with brakes on them should take their place. The airdrome itself should have its identifying mark, either a number or some distinctive design. At night there should be a beacon, a revolving one is usually the best. It should have a certain period of revolution so as to indicate which airdrome it is, just as a lighthouse flashes its signal at certain intervals for identification.

One part of the airdrome should be reserved for airplanes to land, indicated by a sign on the ground, usually a letter "T" about twenty by twenty feet, painted white. It may be necessary to reserve several places for the landing of different kinds of airplanes—large ones and small ones, long distance express planes and local service planes. Wherever possible, passengers should be conducted from the airplanes to the streets through underground passages so as not to obstruct the field.

Traffic officers should always be on duty to handle the planes, signalling them when to land, where to land, when and where to take off. Such signals are usually given by flags. Airplanes should be removed from the flying field as soon as possible after landing. Immediately upon coming to rest at the appointed place, either at a hangar or at the side of the airdrome, the airplane pilot should receive his orders from the Operations Office on the airdrome, or he should go to the Operations Office and report.

This office corresponds to a train despatcher's office on a railroad. On the walls should be maps and diagrams of the various airways going out from the port. On these maps, the position of all air-

FIELDS AND AIRWAYS

planes flying the route should be constantly noted. These are usually represented by a small model of the airplane whose position is checked every few minutes as it passes a ground station and reports by visual signal, or when it reports directly into a central radio control station. This map also should show the state of the weather and the time at all points on the airway. The temperature, direction of the wind, general weather conditions and cloud ceiling should be shown. The Operations Office should be equipped with radio telegraph which would receive and transmit weather signals, with telephones connecting all along the airway, and with messengers and police sufficient to handle every feature of the airdrome.

Facilities should be provided near each hangar for refuelling airplanes with gasoline, benzol, crude oil, lubricating oils, radiator liquids, ordinary spare parts, tires, electrical fittings, aviator's clothing, parachutes and safety devices and the ordinary mechanic's tools. Sufficient mechanics should be constantly on duty to make any minor repairs necessary. No airplane should be allowed to leave the ground without being given a certificate of airworthiness by the person in charge of the airport. Many accidents are caused by allowing airplanes to take off with one of their engines missing a little, or with the controls jamming a little, when these things are not thought to be of enough seriousness to require attention, just as leaky vessels are sometimes allowed to put out to sea, and when they get out in the broad Atlantic, they sink.

Besides the radio beacon, there should be a loop of wire surrounding the airdrome, to send out radio impulses when an airplane comes over in a fog. The plane can be directed straight to the airdrome by the radio beacon. It can be signalled from the ground whether to land, and when it begins spiraling down it can tell as soon as it crosses the loop whether it is on the edge of the airdrome or inside the loop. This can be told within 200 feet, one way or another. We have now developed altimeters almost to the point where they will tell us when the ground is within thirty feet under us. If a modern airplane with good landing gear levels off at thirty feet, it can "mush" down to the ground without an accident.

To take off, an airplane should go to that part of the field allotted for outgoing planes, moving to that position around the edge of the airdrome, not across it. The pilot will have made himself familiar in the Operations or Traffic Office with all the marks in that vicinity which will help him. The airdrome should have a long arrow drawn in the

FIELDS AND AIRWAYS

direction each airway lies from it. For instance, if the airplane is leaving an airdrome near New York to go to Chicago, as soon as the pilot gets in the air he need not look at his compass for direction but can look at the ground and see an arrow marked with the word "Chicago" pointing in that direction; or if he wants to go to Jacksonville, Florida, he can follow the Jacksonville arrow.

The pilot should have received his instructions on which way to turn as he leaves the ground, whether to the right or left, and to what altitude he should rise before proceeding on his way. The direction of turning given to the pilot on taking off should be opposite to the direction of turning assigned to airplanes which are to land on the field, so they will keep entirely clear of each other. Whether that will be to the right or left depends of course on the direction of the wind, and the position of obstructions on the airdrome.

Air fields should be provided with fire fighting equipment of all kinds, with surgical assistance, with proper waiting rooms, restaurants and everything necessary for the handling of aeronautical traffic. For a person accustomed to handling military aircraft, an airdrome is easy to organize for the handling of civil and commercial aviation, because comparatively few airplanes are concerned.

Being near cities or ground transportation lines, the features of supply, that is, the procuring of fuel and material, is comparatively easy. A permanent installation may be effected and constantly improved.

In military aviation, however, any ordinary field on the side of a mountain or in a swamp may have to be occupied by hundreds of airplanes with almost no preparation. During the last war, at the battle of St. Mihiel, I had 1400 airplanes. In some places we had to despatch several hundred at a time from the same field. They all had to be supplied with ammunition, fuel and spare parts, with food and medical attendance for the men. These units had to move on the minute, by day or by night, and the greatest experience, care and attention was required of the officers handling them. Men cannot be taught how to do things of this kind except by long practice under war conditions. The principles followed are along the same general lines I have laid out for the handling of an airdrome. The airplanes take off at the same time by the hundreds and land in large groups and formations, sometimes at minute intervals, so it can be appreciated how precisely everything must be done.

At night when an airplane comes over an airdrome, it signals either by flashing a light, shooting

Equipment on a Transcontinental Flying Field

Floodlights Illuminating an Airdrome at Night

FIELDS AND AIRWAYS

a rocket or reporting by radio that it desires to land. It also notifies the airdrome where it is from and what kind of a plane it is. Orders are then given it, either to land or to remain in the air at a certain altitude for a given time until other planes have landed.

Suitable lights are provided on an airdrome so that the pilot of a plane can see the ground. While nearly any light will do for a well-trained pilot, usually it is best to land along the beam of a searchlight or to have the light shining from one side or both sides on the airdrome. The same signals that are used in the daytime to indicate wind, direction of landing or takeoff, appear at night illuminated.

When the pilot takes off from the airport, he continues his flight along the airway. This to an airplane is much the same as a cross country road is to an automobile. Before we had roads across country, with good surfaces, with gasoline stations every few miles and garages at which repairs could be made, traffic by automobile was quite difficult, if not impossible. In a corresponding way, without properly organized airways, air traffic is difficult and dangerous. An airway may consist of a route marked in the simplest way, with very few facilities, or it may correspond almost to a road like the Lincoln Highway.

I have often flown along the Lincoln Highway and pictured to myself an airway from New York to San Francisco, consisting of a road about five hundred feet wide, lighted at night, where an airplane could land at any time or place. Indications of the weather could be put down on the ground by visual signals or transmitted by radio. The surface of the road would be painted a bright yellow with a white streak in the middle so it could be seen to the best advantage through fogs, storms or at night. A pilot could take his cargo over such an airway with the minimum risk. He could land wherever occasion required, whether on account of weather, a broken part, to replenish his fuel or to take on and discharge passengers or goods. But the construction of such an airway would be very expensive. Various degrees approaching it have been installed in Europe and the United States.

One of the first airways installed in this country, during the war, was provided largely through the efforts of Mr. Carl Fisher and extended from Indianapolis to Dayton, Ohio. Indications were painted on the tops of buildings to show the points of the compass and the direction Dayton and Indianapolis were from each other. Night flying had not yet been taken up so there were no lights on this airway. Immediately after the war, I had a model

FIELDS AND AIRWAYS

airway put in between Washington and Dayton, equipped with all the means necessary for through traffic so that others desiring to put in airways across country would have a pattern to follow. This airway included weather service, radio stations, night lights and a system of airdromes.

An airway must provide not only a means for the pilot to follow it easily and to land safely in case of trouble, but also a system for keeping track of the airplane from the ground, so as to radio instructions to the pilot and to locate the plane in case it is not heard from and does not arrive at its destination. There is no excuse today for an airplane crashing into a mountain while flying through a storm, or getting lost in a cross-country flight. Often chances have to be taken, particularly in carrying mail or in military operations, but along a well-organized airway, with proper airplanes, through traffic can be made more safe than automobile transport, just as safe as a railroad and almost as safe as sea transport.

A good airway should have identification marks in sight of each other in ordinary weather, that is, every five or ten miles. This mark may take the form of a circle on the ground or an arrow pointing onward. We have even thrown out bags of lime, which when dumped, scattered over the ground and made a white mark that remained a long time.

Good fields should be laid out and marked every twenty-five miles. Three general classes of fields should be provided: first, the airport where all facilities for handling air traffic are to be found, corresponding to the great transportation terminals of railroads in the cities; next, local airports with radio and telephone facilities, where fuel, water and small repairs can be obtained; third, a landing field where only telephone facilities and a wind indicator exist.

All fields into which a plane could enter in case of necessity should be marked. Those in which a good landing can be made should be marked with the letter "T," and those in which a safe landing is somewhat problematical should be marked with a cross. These latter are popularly known as "crash fields."

A revolving beacon should be provided at the twenty-five-mile intervals, for night flying. Between these points, preferably where landing fields exist, there should be other fixed lights, either flashlights from gas accumulators or red lights, in accordance with the character of the field. The most careful marking should be made on the airway in the vicinity of mountains, or where roads, railroads

FIELDS AND AIRWAYS

or other channels of transportation are few and far between. A strip map of the airway should always be carried in the airplane, and even passengers should be provided with information of the route in printed form so they would know what they were seeing.

Airplanes of course should be heated and all comforts provided for. One very efficient method of heating airplanes built of metal tubing is for the exhaust gases to be led back through the tubes. They can be turned on or off by a valve, whenever a change of temperature is desired.

As the pilot flies along the airway, he should receive information from the ground as to the state of the weather ahead of him. If there are storms or fog in his path, he should either be ordered to turn aside to another airway or advised that conditions are such that he can fly through safely.

With the airplanes that will be built in the near future, after the machine is once taken into the air and set on its course, it can be turned over to the automatic pilot, the gyroscopic instrument which handles the controls and holds the airplane on its way. All the flyer will have to do with this instrument is to keep watch on how the wind is affecting him, whether it is blowing him sideways or whether he can hold the course without change. If he gets into a fog or storm, he has to rely on his compasses and on the radio beacon which lies at the airdrome toward which he is flying because all means of seeing the ground or other identifications are lost. He reports by radio the number of his plane as he passes over the various airway stations. When he nears his destination, he consults an instrument which indicates to him when he is over the airport and begins gliding toward the earth.

At present if the cloud ceiling is a few hundred feet high, the pilot has no difficulty in landing either by day or night, but if the fog reaches to the ground, he is not able to make his landing with certainty. Within a few years, there is no question but that altimeters will have been perfected which will indicate exactly how many feet beneath him the ground is, so he can level off and come to earth in safety. When this is accomplished air transport will become one of the safest means of human locomotion.

CHAPTER VII

COMMERCIAL AVIATION

COMMERCIAL aviation is that branch of aeronautics in which aircraft are employed to carry passengers or goods for profit. So far, the cost per pound mile for aircraft transport is very much greater than on railroads or steamships, but the speed is from five to ten times as great, therefore those who put a premium on speed will use air transportation.

Accurate figures on the actual cost of transportation by air are difficult to obtain because in most countries commercial aviation is subsidized by the government, and passenger fare is made to correspond to the fares on railroads and ships. In the United States, there is no direct subsidy to passenger carrying lines, but the mail contracts greatly assist certain lines that are beginning to open a commercial service.

It appears that it costs about as much to carry one pound of freight one mile in an airplane as to carry one ton a mile in a railroad train, or about 2000 to 1. The tractive effort necessary to pull an airplane through the air is more than ten times as great per pound of gross weight as by a freight train. The train will coast on a 2 percent grade, whereas a plane requires about a 20 percent grade. The unit fuel consumption is about ten times as great for the airplane and the cost ratio may be even greater because the locomotive burns a very low grade fuel and the airplane a very high grade gasoline. The crew of a train carrying hundreds of tons of freight is five to six men. The crew of a weight carrying airplane averages over one and a half men for each ton carried. At present airplanes are no faster for distances less than 500 miles than the existing railroad system, taking into consideration the time required to go from the average airdrome to the city, usually an hour's drive, and the delays incident to embarking and disembarking.

If transportation terminals could be constructed in centers of population, this drawback would be eliminated. Under present conditions, night service as well as day service for passengers and goods is a necessity, otherwise competition with existing transportation systems is difficult. A good instance of this is traffic between New York and Chicago. If airplanes fly only in the daytime, there is little saving in time as the trip by train only requires one night and part of a day, the daylight portion being no longer than that required by airplane. If however passengers board an airplane at ten o'clock at night, they would be in Chicago by daylight the

COMMERCIAL AVIATION

next morning and be ready to do business at 8 o'clock. The time saved in this instance would be quite an advantage.

In comparison with steamships, which move at less than half the speed of trains, the advantages would be proportionately greater.

Regularity of schedule along well organized airways approximates that of railroads or steamers. Heavy fogs and storms sometimes delay railroads and steamers to an even greater extent than they delay aircraft. An airplane can fly through a sixty-mile wind with comparative ease, where a steamship would have to heave to and be in grave danger of foundering.

The cost per passenger mile in airplanes is anywhere from 9¢ to 60¢. The development of larger aeronautical engine units, more economical fuel and more efficient propellors will reduce the cost of operation. Not only has the development of commercial aviation been deterred by the huge operating costs, but also from a lack of knowledge of what articles could be carried at a profit in the air. Wherever air lines are to be established, a thorough survey should first be made to determine what these articles are, what the demand for their transportation will be and how much can be expected on each trip. If a full load is not carried in the airplane, the cost per pound is greatly increased. Even now, companies are establishing air lines between places where no real airways exist, and where no accurate estimate has been made of the costs involved, of commodities that can be carried or of the difficulties to be encountered. When projects are laid out like this, it is very much like attempting to operate a railway at a profit between two points in the desert where there is nothing to carry and no place to go.

Aside from their use on regular passenger and express lines, aircraft are employed extensively in what might be termed service aviation, for such purposes as photographic surveys; eliminating insect pests such as the boll weevil in cotton, locusts and others; on timber and soil surveys; in advertising, with smoke writing, painted with signs or illuminated at night. Some automotive companies find it quite advantageous to make airplanes and operate them even at a loss on account of the advertising value to the rest of their output. In the Far North, airplanes are used in mine prospecting, in moving furs, gold and other precious articles of light weight, in exploration and rescue work, and a rapid transportation of officials of large operating companies from place to place.

In other communities, there are "jitney" services,

COMMERCIAL AVIATION

which carry passengers for short hauls where quick movement is necessary and other means of transport are deficient. This is particularly the case in the oil fields of our southwest, where oil machinery needs rapid repair and where inspectors are constantly going from place to place. One of my old officers runs a service of this kind, charging 30 cents a mile for his airplanes which carry two people and 50 pounds of baggage each. This service has been very well handled for five years, with no loss of life, very little loss of material and at an excellent profit.

Aircraft transportation is much more comfortable and pleasant than any other form of travel. In well-ventilated cabin planes going around 130 miles per hour, the motion due to rough air is not as perceptible as on railroads or steamers. Airplanes can be made practically noiseless, with no vibrations. There is a total absence of dust, smoke or cinders, and the well-upholstered seats and sleeping berths can be made as comfortable as any.

As soon as the gyroscopic automatic pilot comes into general use, and when altimeters and radio control systems are perfected so airplanes can land in fogs, there will be a tremendous development of passenger service by air. People will have learned by that time of the safety of air travel and will be willing to pay well for the increased speed.

Civil aviation is that branch of aeronautics which handles certain activities of the civil branches of the government, of which the U. S. Air Mail Service is an example. It does not generally come into competition with commercial aviation and therefore its value depends upon the results obtained instead of on the actual dollars and cents realized from its operation.

The Air Mail Service not only cuts down the time across the continent for the ordinary letter from five days to thirty-six hours, but is especially valuable to banks, as the time element is the great cost burden on business transactions. Every added hour in the transit of any article adds to the cost of business in man hours of work, in interest carrying charges on commercial paper and consequently entails additional capital assets. As banking deals extensively with interest payments which depend on time, the shortening of the time of transportation results in a great saving.

During the year 1929, the American people poured a great deal of money into commercial aviation. Factories were started which soon overstocked the market. Airlines, carrying passengers and freight, were put into operation with plenty of capi-

COMMERCIAL AVIATION

tal but with poorly thought out systems and with little or no investigation as to what returns there would be on the money invested.

On January 15, 1930, the Postmaster General gave out the following statement:

"There are at present approximately 200 planes and 250 expert pilots engaged in the air mail service. The twenty-five domestic air mail contractors, over regular routes aggregating 14,368 miles, are flying approximately 40,500 miles each twenty-four hours, about 60 per cent of which is flown at night. During the first year of operation under the contract system, 473,100 pounds of air mail were carried. During the last year 5,636,660 pounds were carried.

Many of these lines were planned and equipped in accord with the best practice of the flying art; others were less well considered. But the experience of all in 1929 was substantially the same. With a paying load of only 16 to 40 per cent of capacity, all closed the year with operating deficits so great that the very life of the passenger transport industry today is in the balance.

It is significant that the only air passenger carriers who have apparently been able to make a profit are the ones who have been carrying passengers on short flights of from ten to thirty minutes. When our people have made a few practice flights, when they have passed the toddling stage in the air, I believe they will be ready for their air marathons. But can the air passenger carriers hold out until that day comes?

And how did the air mail contractors fare in 1929? The answer is, variously, depending upon several factors. Air mail contracts, to which reference has been made, were awarded pursuant to the provisions of the Act of Congress approved June 3, 1926. That law in substance provides that the Postmaster-General may contract for the transportation of air mail by aircraft between such points as he may designate, on a poundage basis, not exceeding $3 per pound, without regard to the distance travelled.

The disparity between the compensations paid various contractors will appear from a few examples. The rate from Boston to New York is $3 per pound; from New York to

Chicago, 86 cents per pound; from Chicago to Salt Lake City, $1.95 per pound; from Salt Lake City to Los Angeles, $3 per pound; from Atlanta to Chicago, 78 cents per pound, and from Cleveland to Pittsburgh, $3 per pound. If the route is one over which air mail flows in large volume, the contractor has generally been prosperous. If, on the other hand, the volume transported is small, the contractor has fared poorly. In some instances air-mail contractors are also operating passenger services, using the profits derived from mail operations to offset the losses incurred in passenger operations.

The over-production of airplanes by the aviation industry will of course correct itself. The situation, however, in which the air transport industry finds itself may properly occasion the deepest public concern. If that industry should collapse because of lack of public support for the passenger lines, the millions which the government has contributed to encourage commercial aviation, as well as a large part of the public's investment in the aviation industry, will be lost.

Is there a solution to this problem? If Congress, which has always been ready to aid aviation, will give to the Post Office Department the authority, and if we may have the unreserved cooperation of the air transport industry, we believe a solution is at hand. In our judgment, the method of determining the compensation of air-mail contractors must be revolutionized.

The system of paying by the pound regardless of distance traveled is manifestly unsound. Such a system compels the contractor to gamble on the volume of mail he will carry and creates an inducement for him to swell his volume by unethical practices. He is obliged to make his flight whether the Postoffice Department furnishes him one pound or a thousand pounds of mail, and he should therefore be paid a just compensation for his readiness to serve, as well as for his service performed.

The Postoffice Department recommends that the act of June 3, 1926, as amended May 17, 1928, be amended so as to authorize the Postmaster General to contract for the transportation of mail by aircraft between such points as he may designate at fixed rates per mile for definite weight spaces, the base rate not to exceed $1 per mile for 1500 pounds of mail capacity.

Under such an authorization, a schedule of compensation could be set up providing for the payment of perhaps 30 cents per mile for a weight space of 100 pounds, with increased compensation per mile for increasing weight space, until the maximum of $1 per mile for 1500 pounds of weight space is reached. It is probable that to the base rates per mile a proper factor should be added for night flying and for flying over mountains or territory frequently covered by fog.

It will be seen that this innovation would greatly increase the air mail service to the public by permitting the dispatch of air mail on regularly scheduled passenger flights. At the same time, it would enable the Postoffice Department to give immediate assistance to air passenger carriers on such routes as were deemed essential, by paying for carrying the mails a substantial sum, based upon a definite weight space preempted.

The Postmaster General should further be authorized by negotiation with present air mail contractors to extend air mail contracts to a maximum period of ten years from the date of the original award, at a compensation not in excess of the legal maximum. With the passenger lines, as with the exclusively mail lines, preference, if possible, in the awarding of contracts should be given to pioneers in the air transport industry of good character and financial responsibility.

At the present time the Postoffice Department in compensation paid to its mail contractors, the Department of Agriculture through the medium of its weather service, and the Department of Commerce by lighting airways, providing emergency landing fields and supervising commercial flying, are contributing in the aggregate more than $30,000,000 annually to the cause of civil aeronautics.

In my judgment, progressively to extend the aid of these three departments to air mail and passenger lines covering the entire map of the United States would create an unjustifiable tax burden. For the present it would seem sufficient for the Federal Government to concentrate its exceptional aid on essential air transportation routes, that is to say, routes that have been traveled by ox team, pony express, railroad, automobile and airplane since white men have inhabited North America."

Nowhere in the world do airplane lines carrying passengers and freight on a large scale make a profit out of their operations without a subsidy

from the Government. In the United States, contracts for carrying the mail are virtually a subsidy. The nations of Europe, realizing that the greatest benefit from a commercial air service at present would be its use in time of war, subsidize all lines that carry passengers and freight on the basis of the kind of airplanes used, the number of pilots and mechanics each company has, its hangars, repair shops and equipment.

In most countries, any group of men wishing to start an airplane company apply to the Department of the Air for a charter giving them the privilege of operation over certain routes, and a subsidy. If they use, for instance, an airplane suitable for bombardment in case of war, the government will pay half the cost of the airplane, half the salaries of the pilots and mechanics, and will give a certain amount of money for each mile flown and for each passenger carried. In return for this, the company must hold its airplanes and men ready to be called out in case of war. It has to keep its equipment in good shape to make it safe for the travelling public and it has to charge rates which will not be substantially higher than those charged by railways or ships over the same routes, including transfer service, cab fares, meals and sleeping cars. Certain companies are also guaranteed a stated income on their investment if the subsidy alone does not give them a reasonable return.

Aeronautical insurance plays a large part in successful commercial air enterprises. At the present time, there is very little reliable data on the subject, because the industry is so young and enough time has not yet elapsed for the compilation of statistics on accidents, fatalities and damages caused in or by aircraft.

Certain companies will write insurance for aircraft but naturally charge rather high premiums. Aviation insurance may be obtained covering fire, theft, windstorm, damage or public liability, much the same as with automobiles. Slightly different policies are issued for airport and passenger liability. One leading company writes fire insurance in three different ways: Under all circumstances except fire resulting from crash; under all circumstances including fire from crash; and fire occurring only while the plane is on the ground. The first classification carries a reasonable premium, usually from 3 per cent to 7 per cent of the face of the policy, depending on the hangar used, the type of plane and motor, and fire precautions. The premium on the second is extremely high. This may be due to the fact that fire so often follows a crash, but the reason advanced by the insurance company is the frequency with which a plane went up in flames after a crash when it was covered by such a policy. "This," they said, "seemed to be the only instance in which the assured had read their policies carefully." The third form is mainly for the use of manufacturers or dealers in aircraft.

Insurance against wind storms only covers the plane while on the ground, whether in or out of the hangar. The "damage" policy usually covers only self-inflicted damage, as when a plane crashes, and does not cover damage caused by another plane or object. Its cost ranges between 10 per cent and 17 per cent of the value of the aircraft. For property damage, another policy must be taken out which is similar to an automobile policy of this character and does not cover one's own plane. Public liability insurance protects the owner of a plane or fleet of planes against any legal liability to the public (not including passengers) for injuries or death due to an accident caused by his plane. The insurance company is liable, however, only for the limits of the policy. Another policy insures the lives of passengers carried, on which the premium is considerably lower if they are not carried for profit. On a $5000 policy, if passengers are carried for hire, the premium would be about $300; if not, the premium would be $200.

There are special policies which cover the legal liability of an airport for any accident occurring on or about it. These are often written for short periods, as when a race meet is to be held, or any other occasion when crowds are expected.

Insurance covering flying risks may be issued at a flat rate or on a "per flying hour" basis. In the latter, the premium is based on the number of hours flown during the life of the policy, and monthly reports are required to be made.

Insurance companies cannot afford to assume anything, or take too long chances. Their computations must be based on facts and fully reliable statistics; consequently, the fact that they are insuring men engaged in aviation at a constantly diminishing premium, and are placing no restrictions on air travel by their policy holders "in a licensed airplane operated by a licensed pilot upon a regular passenger route between definitely established airports," argues much for the increased safety of this form of travel.

CHAPTER VIII

INSTRUMENTS

FEW of us realize how primitive are the aircraft of today compared to what they will be not many years hence. Already improvements have been introduced that will totally change our means of air transportation in appearance, in its factors of safety and comfort, and in methods of operation. These changes do not come all of a sudden but have to be worked out in slow steps and minute calculations by persons with expert knowledge of what is required.

The reading public gleans most of its aeronautical knowledge from thrilling accounts of flights across the land, the seas or the wastes of the Arctic, or from reports of ghastly accidents where the crew and passengers of the plane are killed in a crash or burned in the air. They still look on flying as a dangerous and hair-raising adventure, pursued only by those who have a fearless disposition. Nobody takes the trouble to explain to them the mechanical wonders that go to make up a modern flying machine. They know little of the absorbingly interesting activity ceaselessly going on behind the curtain, that spells progress.

INSTRUMENTS

As a matter of fact, the public has not yet been taken into the confidence of the initiated few by whom the principles of aviation are thoroughly understood; for one reason, because those who are developing the newest instruments do not want the public to know what they are working on until their equipment is perfected and patented. Many think that the public would not understand these things even if they were told about them. The automobile, however, has made almost everyone a mechanic and people are now in a position to understand things which a few years ago would have been entirely too technical for the average lay mind. Among the younger generation especially, boys from twelve to twenty, the airplane is better understood than was the automobile by those who are now middle aged.

If a person glances into the cockpit of an airplane, he is at once struck with the great number of instruments that appear in front of the pilot's seat. Some of these are very necessary while others might well be done away with.

In the early days of flying, all pilots were taught to fly without instruments and to judge by eye their distance from the ground, by ear how their engine was going and by the feel of the air against their face or the sound in the wires how fast they were going. Nowadays more and more dependence is being placed in instruments instead of "feel." This is a good thing in some ways, particularly in fogs or storms or when flying an airplane with a closed cabin. On the other hand, no instrument can make up for the human factor, and many a crash today results from the pilot not feeling the air, and being so closed in that he cannot tell except by his instruments when the airplane is going into a stall.

The most important instrument in the airplane is the tachometer or revolution counter. This is merely a dial with one hand, attached to a flexible cable connected with the main shaft of the engine by a spur gear, and it indicates the number of revolutions at which the engine is going. With this instrument the pilot is able to tell more about the condition of his engine than with any other thing. From the number of revolutions the engine makes, he knows approximately the speed at which he is doing. If the revolution counter fluctuates up and down, say from 800 to 1200 R.P.M., he knows there is some trouble with his engine; or if the revolutions constantly diminish, this also is an indication of trouble. In testing out his airplane on the ground before flying, to see if it is in good condition, he relies principally on his tachometer to tell if the engine is delivering its power.

The instrument next in importance is the oil

INSTRUMENTS

pressure gauge which shows whether the oil is circulating through the engine properly. With machines that have to work as fast as the aviation engine, the least defect in lubrication is a serious matter.

The third most important instrument is the thermometer which indicates the temperature of the liquid that is cooling the engine. If the temperature rises too high, this shows either that there is trouble in the engine or that the weather is so hot the radiator is not big enough to cool the cylinders properly. If it registers too low, either the radiating surface is too large or the weather is too cold, and shutters should be put over the radiator to reduce the surface. Either extreme of temperature may result in stopping the engine.

Besides these three essential instruments, there are a multitude of others. There is the air speed indicator which usually takes the form of a small tube placed ahead of the leading edge of the wings, away from the propellor wash so the air can blow on it freely. The air pushing into the tube presses on a little rubber diaphragm with a spring arrangement in it which acts on the indicator, causing it to show the speed at which the airplane is moving through the air. These indicators are quite accurate and when working properly will show the pilot when the plane is approaching a stall or losing flying speed.

The altimeter or aneroid barometer indicates the approximate height at which the ship is flying. This instrument depends for its operation on the pressure of the air against a little vacuum chamber connected up by a set of levers to the indicator. It measures the height of the air above one, not the height of the column of air under the plane. As the top of our atmosphere is composed of waves very much like those in the ocean, but bigger, the height of the column of air constantly varies. Usually when the sun shines in the morning, the air expands and the column of air is higher, so the barometer indicates a higher reading than there should be. In the afternoon, the reverse is the case. When a low pressure area is entered the barometer may have an error of 1000 feet or more, or when an area of high barometric pressure is entered it may register 1000 feet too high.

These instruments can be made to show very small differences in altitudes. For instance with a well calibrated altimeter, one may walk from the first floor to the second in a house and the difference will be indicated. Very sensitive ones used to be made for use in free balloons so as to tell the instant the balloon's weight became greater than the air and

INSTRUMENTS

it began to sink, so ballast could be thrown out to keep it up.

Altimeters have to be corrected every time the airplane lands or takes off. They are not accurate enough for landing in fogs although attempts have been made to give them corrections by radio from the ground. This has been done with some success experimentally. Within its limits, the altimeter is quite a satisfactory instrument.

A great deal of experimentation is being carried on with electrical altimeters which will tell the exact distance the airplane is from the ground, but these have not yet been entirely perfected.

The magnetic compass as arranged for an airplane is much the same as the mariner's compass. The magnetized needles are usually in clusters and suspended in a liquid which absorbs the vibration due to the engine. The compass is placed where it can be readily seen by the pilot but where it will be least affected by the movable masses of metal in the engine and the electrical connections that form the ignition system. In the northern hemisphere, the northern end of the needle tends to dip down toward the pole therefore the south end must be weighted so the needle will rest horizontally in the compass case. However, when the needle is pushed away from the north, the extra weight on the south end throws it out of balance and it dips down in the other direction. As long as the magnetic compass is held level in an airplane, it works quite well but if the plane is inclined over to one side, or spins or dives steeply, the compass is thrown out of dynamic and magnetic balance and the whole contraption begins to whirl and spin and becomes useless. When using the compass, the pilot has to be careful to keep his ship on an even keel and to take every advantage that the ground offers him to check its accuracy by taking a sight on some prominent object, the direction of which he knows, and comparing it with his compass reading.

But newer instruments to indicate direction are taking the place of the magnetic compass. One of the best, evolved in the last ten years, is called the earth inductor compass. In searching for a new system of determining direction, we tried many contrivances and at last attacked the problem from the standpoint that the earth was a magnet, surrounded by lines of electrical force, which if cut by another wire, would cause a current to be generated in that wire, just as is induced in an electric generator when the armature is rotated through the field of the magnet. We found we could get a current from the earth which, although feeble, could be detected

INSTRUMENTS

on a sensitive galvanometer. Thus the earth inductor compass came into being. It is a simple and accurate instrument, consisting of a coil of wire which, when it cuts the lines of force from the earth, will have a current produced in it strong enough to be indicated on a galvanometer. If the airplane flies parallel to these lines of force, no current will be generated in the coil and there will be no indication on the galvanometer. What we do is to set the compass according to the direction we want to go, so the dial will read zero, then watch the needle. As long as it stays at zero, it gives us our true course. If it goes to the right, the airplane is flying too far to the right and must be corrected by turning it to the left. Not only can a straight course be set on this compass, but it can also be used on a Great Circle course, over the edge of the earth, where direction must be changed every hour or two. In this case the pilot refers to a table made out for the trip, showing when the course should be changed.

No matter how the airplane may be inclined to one side or the other, or even upside down, this instrument will read just the same. The only possibility for an error would be if the pilot made a complete half circle, 180 degrees and started going back the other way, in which case the compass would again read zero.

Gyroscopic compasses have also been used in airplanes but their great weight has militated against their general application.

Various instruments have been devised to indicate to the pilot whether or not the airplane is flying level. These have been made in the form of pendulums, spirit levels or little ground steel balls contained in tubes. All depend for their operation on the force of gravity. If an airplane is flying on a straight course and dips its right wing down, the gravity instruments will incline in that direction and a true indication will be given of the airplane's attitude. However, if the plane is flying along on an even keel and a quick turn is made to the left without banking, then the centrifugal force will carry the gravity instruments over to the right and an indication will be given that the airplane is inclined to the right whereas it may be inclined in the opposite way entirely. These instruments are by no means accurate but like the aneroid barometer give only a relative indication, and may give a positively wrong one.

In flying through fogs, it is necessary to keep the airplane on an even keel. The pilot must have some point of reference on which he can align the plane.

INSTRUMENTS

If he could see a horizontal line in front of him which kept its position, or a vertical line, such as a church steeple, he would have no trouble keeping the airplane in proper trim. An instrument that has been devised for this purpose is the gyroscopic turn indicator, which depends for its action on a small gyroscope which is actuated and kept spinning at the rate of about 22,000 revolutions a minute by a column of air taken in through a tube. As long as this little gyroscope is kept spinning, it will remain in a certain position and if any deviation is made to the right or left of the gyroscope which is set in an up and down position, it will give an indication immediately. It is connected with a dial which indicates instantly whether a turn is being made to the right or left. In other words, this gyroscope sets up a vertical line for the pilot to fly toward. This instrument is also equipped with another gyroscope placed horizontally which indicates if the airplane's nose is pointed down or up. If these gyroscopic turn indicators are working properly, the pilot is able to fly in fog and maintain his direction with great accuracy. The trouble with them is that they depend for their action on the pressure of air through a tube to keep them spinning and should this tube become clogged with snow or sleet, or sometimes even rain, the action of the instruments will be stopped.

Arrangements for lighting the instruments for night flying are important. This is accomplished by painting the instruments with radium paint, or by lighting them by electricity in the way that instruments on the dashboard of an automobile are illuminated. Airplanes that fly at night carry electric spotlights which can be shone on the ground and that on a clear night will show the earth several hundred feet ahead. They may be equipped with calcium flares under the wings which are set off by electricity and which also illuminate a large area of ground. Some planes carry flares attached to parachutes which can be dropped off, illuminating a large area of ground, in some cases a mile or two in diameter, thus giving the pilot an opportunity to fly around and select the best place to come down.

For high altitude work, airplanes are equipped with tanks of oxygen either in liquid form or compressed into tubes. The average man needs an additional supply of oxygen at about 20,000 feet. This may be inhaled either through a tube put into the mouth or through a tube connecting with a mask placed over the face. The gas supply may be controlled manually by the pilot who turns a small valve with his hand, or it may be controlled auto-

INSTRUMENTS

matically through an altimeter which will feed more or less gas as the altitude is increased or decreased.

Electricity is used for heating parts of the airplane, for heating the clothing and footgear of the aviator, and for radio telegraph and telephone instruments. The electric generator for this power may be connected up to the motor or set off on the wing and actuated by air pressure. Of course when the airplane is at rest and there is no air pressure against the wing, this latter system will not work. Some airplanes are equipped so they can put up a radio mast while resting on the ground, and employ radio as well as when they are flying and trailing a wire underneath. Some airplanes have transmitting radio wires placed inside their wings and thus when several planes are flying along together, they are able to talk to each other by telephone. They may talk to the ground also, and be connected through wires to any telephone in the country.

All airplanes should be equipped with self starters as the starting of airplanes by hand is both dangerous and unnecessary. It has resulted in a great many deaths and accidents, particularly when the engine is cold. There are several different types of self starters. Some put compressed air into the cylinders of the engine, and in this way push it around. Others put gas into the cylinders, which is easily ignited. Another starter is like that on the automobile, depending on a small electric motor driven by a storage battery. These have been so heavy that they have seldom been installed on airplanes. Another sort of starter is one operated by hand through a series of gears which greatly multiplies the power applied by the person turning the crank.

Instruments are being developed that will fly the airplane without the touch of human hands. Most of them are mechanical, some are electric. Certain successful ones depend on a gyroscope for this operation. A gyroscope is like a top, spin it fast enough and it will hold its position no matter how the supporting surface of the airplane is tilted. When the airplane moves out of its course, the gyroscope remains steady and is able to apply power to the controls so as to steer the plane back in the direction desired.

Power is transmitted from the gyroscope to the controls in much the same way that force is exerted on the keys of a player piano. When you put a paper roll in the piano, it passes in front of a place where air is applied, which is blown through the little holes in the paper, thus striking the keys and playing the piano. In a similar manner, when the airplane gets off the horizontal or longitudinal axis,

Early Aerial Torpedo Launched Successfully without Human Pilot in 1917

Pilot Equipped for High Altitude Flying

INSTRUMENTS

a stream of air blowing through small holes in the gyroscopic instrument strikes the controls with the strength of a powerful hand, thus affecting the rudder, the ailerons, or whatever is necessary to bring the plane back to its normal position. When we first started the use of gyroscopic controls, this power was so great it was inclined to break the airplane's wings with its force, so it had to be decreased and made more gradual.

When the pilot has taken off, he can turn the plane over to the automatic pilot which will fly it on the desired course with no deviation except that occasioned by the wind. The winds are well enough known so that we can compensate for their effect, or the position can be plotted from radio signals and the plane put back on its course. The automatic pilot can be so constructed that it will even take the airplane off the ground and land it, with no assisting agency.

A gyroscopic control used on many ocean liners is known as the "Iron Quartermaster" or "Metal Mike." The course is set on the gyroscope, which takes hold of the wheel and steers the ship. This mechanism is a comparatively simple thing and entirely practical, as the ship only requires to be steered in one plane, that is, on the surface of the

SKYWAYS

water, in contrast to up, down and horizontally, as in an airplane.

The safety of future flying depends more on the perfecting of our instruments than on any other phase of aeronautical work.

CHAPTER IX

SAFETY DEVICES

An ounce of prevention is worth a ton of cure in the air, not a pound as on the ground. The best way to insure safety in the air is to estimate what may go wrong and make adequate provision against it.

The thing most dreaded in the air is fire. This danger is always present where a highly inflammable, volatile substance is used for fuel. After all these years of research, we are not yet entirely sure what causes all the fires. Backfires in the engine itself often set the carburetor afire. The safeguard against this is to put metal screens over the air intake of the carburetor which will stop the flame, or to run the air intake of the carburetor out into the open air, entirely away from the rest of the engine. Often the breaking of some part about the engine may cause a gasoline leak and this in turn allow the gasoline to pour on a heated exhaust pipe and start a fire. The engine should always be separated from the gas tanks by a solid metal fire wall. The gasoline can be shut off when the engine catches fire, and it will burn itself out, the pilot meantime sliding the ship sideways so as to keep the fire away from the cabins. I have seen pilots use this maneuver and get away with quite serious fires, even when the flames were streaming back from the engine way behind the cockpit.

An accumulation of gas vapors often occur inside the wings which explode and cause fires. In some of the old airplanes, we had some serious explosions before it was found how to ventilate them properly. Fire is very apt to occur in a crash, and here we are not always sure what causes it. We do know that if the gasoline tank is immediately behind the engine and the airplane hits on its nose, spilling the gasoline over the hot engine, especially the hot exhaust, it is apt to catch fire. This does not account for the fact that when an airplane hits in that manner, the gasoline sometimes explodes in just the same way as an airplane bomb. From this we conclude that it must be caused either by highly compressing the mixture of air and gasoline, which is always present in a gasoline tank only partially full, or by metal rubbing against metal and causing heat, which ignites. The high friction of the crash also may generate an electric spark which can ignite the mixture.

We have had somewhat more trouble with gasoline tanks that depend on air pressure for forcing the gasoline through tubes to the carburetor than

SAFETY DEVICES

with those that depend on a gravity feed or on some kind of pumping system. Even removing the gasoline tanks from the vicinity of the engine does not prevent fires in case of a crash. The crashproof tank, however, is a great safeguard. This crashproofing consists of surrounding the tank with a rubberoid and canvas substance which completely encloses it and keeps it from leaking, no matter how the outside of the tank is distorted by a crash. During the war it also prevented flaming bullets from setting fire to the gas, by immediately closing up the hole the bullet made as it went through the tank. With the larger bullets now used, this does not work so well. It is a fact that crashproof tanks cut down very greatly the number of fires in airplanes, and they should be standard equipment.

Many airplanes are arranged so as to dump their gas tanks overboard in case of fire. This is a simple thing, as tanks can be held in on lugs and a lever pulled which will set them free. Unquestionably, the fire hazard will be greatly reduced by the use of Diesel heavy oil engines.

A great many different kinds of fire extinguishers have been devised. They fall into three categories: first, those that attempt to cool off the fire in the way water acts when thrown on the ordinary fire. This method has little or no effect on burning gasoline. Another method is to cover the burning liquid with a film of non-inflammable substance which will keep all air and oxygen away from the fire, and smother it out. There are various foam extinguishers which will do this successfully under certain conditions where the gasoline or oil is contained in a tank. The third method is to surround the burning gasoline with a gas that will combine with the oxygen and make a non-inflammable gas. Without oxygen, the gasoline will not burn. This system is excellent, provided the fire is confined in a given space where air is not readily accessible.

If a serious fire occurs in the air, there is only one way to escape from it and that is to jump out in a parachute. The parachute is the most efficient safety device ever invented for use in an airplane. Parachutes have been known for centuries, but have only been applied for use in aircraft since the war. All of us as children have taken a big umbrella, opened it and jumped off a high chair or a wall and felt how it pulled, or how the wind hit the umbrella and carried it out of our hands. The one difficulty in adapting it for use in an airplane was to arrange and fold it so that it would operate with certainty when called upon to do so.

In balloons, the parachute is folded up in a container like a bucket placed under the balloon. A

SAFETY DEVICES

cord some feet in length is attached to the back of the balloonist and the pressure distributed through straps around shoulders, chest and legs. It is easy to jump clear of a balloon, because compared to a plane it is practically at rest in the air and does not collapse instantaneously as an airplane may do. In a plane, not only do the changes occur instantly, but a person must jump clear of the whole structure before opening his parachute, otherwise it may become entangled in some part of the plane and be prevented from opening, or it may be cut so that it will not work. Airplane parachutes are made so they can be released by the wearers when desired. A man may jump headlong out of the airplane, fall for two or three thousand feet, then pull the release cord.

The American parachutes that have been found the surest contain two parachutes, one a small one about the size of an umbrella which is made with metal springs and folded up directly under the container of the large parachute, to which it is attached. When the cord releasing the parachute is pulled, the small parachute impelled by its springs jumps out and pulls the large parachute after it.

A parachute suitable to hold a man of average weight must be from 16 to 25 feet in diameter. With it, the shock of impact on the ground will be about the same as that experienced when jumping off a wall about ten feet high.

Parachutes are arranged in various ways and may be carried as a seat, as a pack over the shoulders, across the small of the back, in the form of a vest or across the abdomen. Sometimes two parachutes are carried. Ordinarily it requires a vertical drop of ninety feet for the parachute to open and another fifty or sixty feet for the pilot to stop swinging. Usually three large swings are made by a body before it begins to descend vertically. For airplanes flying very rapidly, this distance may be shortened a little because the parachute opens as it goes through the air at the speed of the airplane when the wearer first jumps out. Some men have jumped from airplanes 100 feet above the ground and still lived.

A parachute can be guided on its way down to some extent by pulling on the shrouds in the direction in which a person desires to go. This has the effect of making the surface on that side smaller and the parachute will therefore fall more rapidly in that direction. An expert with a parachute can maneuver himself very well in a drop of a few thousand feet. If considerable wind is blowing, the parachute may drag the man along the ground. Often a knife is provided to cut the shrouds as

Six Men Jumping from Three Airplanes Simultaneously

The Verville Air Coach, One of the Best Types of American Single-Engine Commercial Planes

Refueling Planes While in the Air

SAFETY DEVICES

otherwise a serious accident might occur. An expert parachutist, however, is able to spill the wind out of his parachute when he lands.

If airplanes are acting over water, a life preserver must be part of the equipment also. The parachute container often has sufficient kapok to float the wearer, or it has an air chamber which can be blown up by one's mouth, or it has a little capsule of highly compressed gas which will fill the air chamber when it is punctured.

Parachutes have been made large enough to sustain an airplane, but they take up so much room that so far it has not been practical to equip larger planes with them. However, demonstrations have been made which show that they are able to descend in fogs by this means. It is not entirely beyond the realm of possibility that the wings of airplanes may be made some day so that by opening or spinning around the central axis, they may act as a parachute to bring the plane straight down.

There is practically nothing about an airplane that does not have to be prepared with the utmost caution to insure safety, especially everything connected with the engine. The gas lines, for instance, running from tank to engine, must be entirely free of any substances that may be dissolved by gas. Rubber hose connections which are frequently placed in these lines are often disintegrated by the gasoline. The bits of rubber get into the jets in the carburetor and stop the engine. Water is frequently found in gasoline. It may get into the tanks on account of improper straining of the gasoline. This should always be done through a chamois skin, which will catch any water that may be in the gas. Cold weather may cause a condensation of water inside the tubes that lead to the carburetor. If this water is forced into the carburetor, it may cause the engine to stop. A simple device to forestall this is the water trap, consisting of a little cup a few inches deep, with the intake and outlet for the gas lines coming into the top of it. As the water is heavier than gasoline, it will sink to the bottom of this trap and a little vent at the bottom can be opened from time to time to let the water out.

All the ignition for airplanes should be made in duplicate so that if one set fails the other will work. In the war, many of our engines of the V-type contained duplicate ignition for both sides of the engine so that all four of the ignition systems had to be shot away or destroyed to bring the airplane down. Water cooling systems were made in two parts so that if one were punctured by a bullet, the other could be used.

A great safeguard for air travel will be brought

SAFETY DEVICES

about when the various engines used for motive power are placed in a central engine room and driven through gears on to a single large propellor. Their number and power would be such that one-third of them could be turned out of gear without affecting the flight of the airplane in a horizontal direction. In this way engines could be held in reserve in case of trouble, or could be worked on in the air. There are only two or three airplanes in existence at present in which engines can be really repaired while in flight.

Efficient landing gear, instruments for fog flying and a good weather and radio service may also be considered as important safety devices.

Ninety per cent of the air accidents occur, not from structural defects in airplanes—these are usually quite strong enough—but from stalls, that is, losing flying speed. Many of these accidents occur during storms. The gyroscopic pilot which will fly the airplane itself will be a great safety factor, as it will prevent stalls to an extent and automatically guide airplanes through storms.

Among the many devices that have been tried to prevent stalls, one quite successful contrivance is the Handley-Page wing slot. This so-called slot is placed along the leading edge of the wing. When in normal flight, that is, when the airplane is going fast enough to sustain itself, the slot lies snug against the wing. If the airplane begins to lose speed and the air pressure against the leading edge of the wing diminishes, the springs with which the slot is equipped automatically push it out and away from the wing. This causes a current of air to flow in the aperture between slot and wing, which in turn flows over the top of the wing and assists in maintaining the vacuum which begins to disappear when the plane loses speed. An airplane is sustained not only by the force of air under it but also by a vacuum on top of the wings.

If an airplane begins to stall at a speed of sixty miles, these slots may cut its stalling speed down to forty miles, which will save the airplane from a fall with incident crash, if the pilot makes immediate use of the advantage the slots give him. Slots have very much the same effect as extending or enlarging the surface of the wing, making it capable of sustaining more weight per square foot, and therefore not stalling so soon.

French Airplane Equipped with Slotted Wings Giving It a Slow Speed. The Airplane has a Maximum Speed of 132 Miles per Hour and a Minimum Speed of 43 Miles per Hour

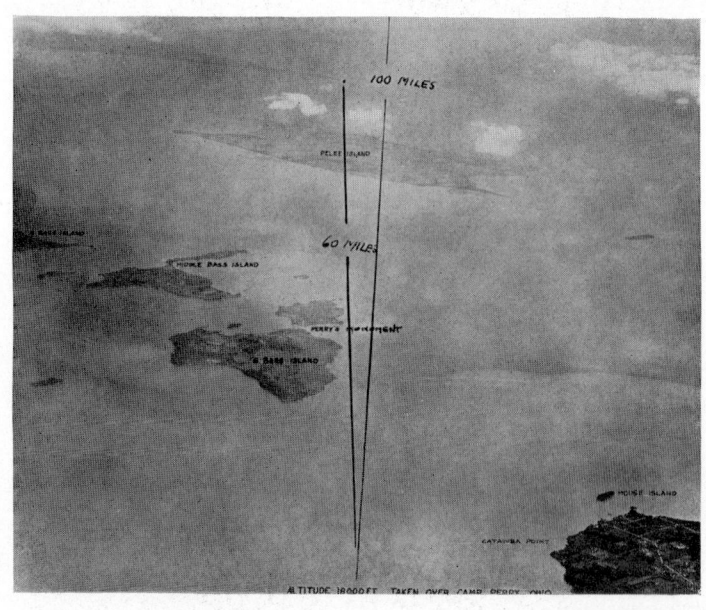

Photograph Taken from an Altitude of Eighteen Thousand Feet Across Lake Erie

CHAPTER X

MAPS

THE aviator finds his way across the country by the assistance of map and compass. A map is a horizontal projection of the earth's surface drawn to scale, that is, a flat picture of the earth on which are indicated the most prominent objects that the aviator will see either by day or night, such as rivers, forests, roads, cities and mountains. The hills and mountains are indicated either by contour lines or hachures.

A contour line indicates the elevation of the ground at a certain height above sea level, or any other altitude taken as a reference, which is called datum.

Suppose that we take a bowl of water and put an egg in it in an upright position, and then raise the water in the bowl a quarter of an inch at a time. Each time we make a mark on the egg with a pencil where the surface of the water touches it. Then if we look straight down at the egg from directly above, we will see the shape of the egg in a horizontal projection; in other words, our contour lines on the egg will show exactly what its shape is and how high it is above the bottom or datum. In this case the contour interval or distance between the contour lines is a quarter of an inch. We are not only able to tell in this way the exact shape of the egg but also its height. The contour lines on hills and mountains are formed in a similar manner; that is, at every hundred, five hundred or thousand feet, a level line is run all around the hill or range of hills indicating the shape and height of the hill or range at that particular point. A person accustomed to reading a map is able to look at one and form a picture in his mind of how the hill or mountain looks in perspective, that is, looked at from the side instead of from the top, as the map shows it. Some men who have piloted airplanes for many years can take a map covering distances of several hundred miles and after looking at it for four or five minutes, go straight to their destination without referring to it again, providing there is good visibility and the ground features can be seen.

Maps are drawn to scale, certain distances on the map equalling certain distances on the ground. One inch on the map may equal one mile, or ten or twenty miles on the ground. The scale of the map may be greater or less in accordance with the amount of detail or number of objects it is desired to show. If drawn to a scale of three inches to the mile, a great many more things may be shown on the map than on one drawn to a scale of one inch to the mile.

A map always shows the position of the cardinal points of the compass, north, south, east and west. All the objects on the map have the same relation to one another as those same objects on the ground have to each other. Thus a person in an airplane may see a high hill to the east. If he places the north of his map toward the north of the earth, then this hill will show directly east on the map.

Hills and slopes may also be represented by hachures, little short lines drawn close together, or by shading, which indicates the shape of hills. Whether they are heavy or light lines indicates whether the slopes are steep or gradual. Usually the tops of these representations of hills are marked by figures indicating their height in feet.

Maps are often executed in natural colors, in which forests are green, rivers are blue, roads yellow, cities or houses black.

While any sort of map may be used by the aviator, special maps have come into general use during the last few years. They are usually long and narrow in form, showing a straight strip of land along the route which the flyer is to take, with a representation of the land for ten or twenty miles on each side of the route. These are called "strip maps."

The cross country flyer sometimes takes an ordinary map and draws a line on it from the town he is in to the place he wants to go. He puts marks on this line at certain distances to indicate where he should be at given times in accordance with the speed of his airplane in still air. If the plane goes 100 miles an hour, it will go 50 miles in half an hour, 150 miles in one hour and a half, and so on.

The compass in the plane is then checked, or "swung," to see that it is pointing properly. This may be done by placing the airplane over the center of a place where north, east, south and west lines are drawn, and then swinging the tail of the plane around to these directions and taking the reading on the compass, noting any error it has from the known. The compass also is checked when the airplane is in the air, by referring it to a north and south line, and an east and west line, such as a road, section line or fence, or a river, because a compass may not point the same in the air as it does on the ground.

When the pilot has reached the altitude at which he will fly, he sets his plane on the required course by his compass and then looks at objects on the ground, to see that these check with his direction.

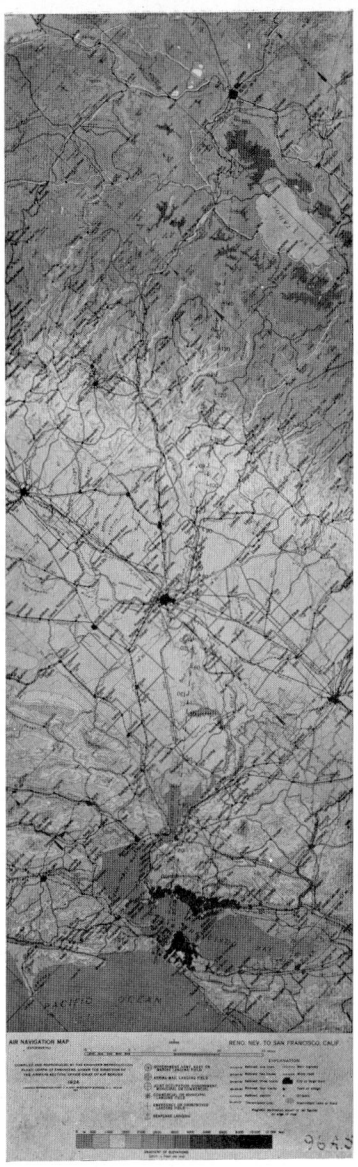

Strip Map for the Use of Air Pilots

BLACKBOARD FOR NOTING WEATHER CONDITIONS AT
VARIOUS FLYING FIELDS

MAPS

When the first half hour elapses, he looks for ground identification points to see exactly where he is. If the first half hour should place him over a river, and instead he finds himself over a town ten miles short of the river, or forty miles out from his starting point, he knows that a wind is blowing against him at a rate of twenty miles an hour and he is actually making only eighty miles an hour ground speed. On another occasion, he may have a wind behind him which carries him ten miles beyond his mark. He may find that he is being blown sideways off his course. If on an east and west course, and he finds the airplane going to the south of the route at a rate of 10 miles per hour, he must point the plane slightly to the north to overcome this and lay a course toward a point 10 miles to the north of his destination at the end of the next hour. In this way he will be brought directly over his objective. If he gets off the course and finds nothing he can recognize definitely beneath him, often he can see a mountain, river or city miles off on one side or the other. If he can see two objects that he can identify on his map, he can take their direction from his airplane by means of the compass, then plot them on his map and in that way approximate his own position in the air by what is called "resection."

While many other instruments have been devised to guide the airplane through the air, ninety nine percent of all flying off established airways is done by the ordinary magnetic compass and map as described above. This method of flying is what we call pilotage, or taking an airplane accurately and carefully from place to place over the surface of the ground where landings may have to be made at any time and where the utmost care is required to find certain small places.

Navigation, on the other hand, is an entirely different thing. That relates to taking an airplane from one place to another over long stretches of water or across the land when one is above the clouds and cannot see identifying objects on the ground. This is really a much simpler matter than pilotage, as the course is figured out ahead of time on a chart. The speed and drift of the wind as compared to the speed of the airplane is estimated and provided for. When a certain time has elapsed, the pilot looks for a ground identification, such as a coast line, light house, mountain or island, which he knows he will pass over if his calculations are true and have been followed without deviation.

So far, with the exception of the dirigible airships and one or two of the larger airplanes, the flights across the Atlantic and Pacific have been made by this simple method.

At first it was supposed that aircraft would have to be navigated by celestial reckoning, using sextant and chronometer for taking the altitude of fixed stars and thus establishing one's position; but this has been proved to be impracticable because the airplane is moving from ten to twenty times as fast as the ordinary vessel, and the platform on which the observation has to be made sways so that it is difficult to make it accurately; also the time required to compute observations is another hindrance because by the time these tables are figured out, the airplane is two or three hundred miles away from that spot.

Fog is the terrible bugbear of the pilot. Although we can fly through fog with our present instruments, we cannot yet land in it with certainty and safety. In flying over mountains, we often encounter a heavy haze or light fog which completely obscures objects on the ground, and we must maintain considerable altitude so as to have plenty of gliding distance in case of a forced landing. In such cases one must fly by dead reckoning and the pilot's ingenuity and knowledge of the air is sometimes taxed to the utmost. He must estimate which way the wind is drifting his airplane, how much it is retarding him, and where his position will be at any given time. If he is flying at different altitudes, the air currents may be quite different at each height. At 2000 feet the wind may be blowing ten miles an hour from one direction, at 8000 feet at twenty-five miles from another direction, and at 12,000 feet at forty or fifty miles.

On one cross-country flight I made from the middle states to Washington, the last ground identification I obtained was at Zanesville, Ohio, 325 miles from Washington. The Allegheny Mountains were covered with clouds that lay thick upon them, so I went up to an altitude of 14,000 to go over them. I had previously learned by telephone that the cloud ceiling in the vicinity of Washington was between two and three thousand feet. All I had to fear was a stoppage by my single motor while going over the Alleghenies, in which case I would have had to land in the clouds which formed a fog on the ground, and probably crashed. From a study of the weather map, it had been estimated that the wind would change at various altitudes and I laid my plans to fly accordingly, changing course a few degrees on the compass at the time the wind should change. When I estimated that the plane was over Washington, I started to come down in long spirals and after passing through three strata of clouds, each a couple of thousand feet thick, I came out of the last directly over the Potomac River and about 8 miles below Washington. This was very accurate piloting with merely a magnetic compass and a map.

Often we lose our way and I have gotten as much as two hundred miles off in a trip of 500 miles. Sometimes this occurs because a compass develops a big error while in the air and a ground identification is mistaken, such as one city for another. Or we may encounter a very heavy head or side wind which we did not estimate for accurately.

Frequently when running out of gas we have had to land in out of the way places, in the mountains or deserts. I remember once landing in the mountains within eight miles of a postoffice, but the mountaineers we met did not know that such a place existed. Neither did they know the name of the President of the United States, or even of the sheriff of their county.

Radio navigation has taken the place of celestial navigation. The radio is used in three ways to fix the airplane's position. The radio beacon or beam is used for giving direction to an airplane. This beam is sent out from a station, just as the light shines out from a lighthouse on the coast. The airplane is directed toward it and an instrument in the plane shows when it is flying straight toward the beam or when it is going to the right or left. As long as the instrument works, the airplane can be held steadily and surely on its course. Another method is to have two or more stations send out signals at the same time to the airplane which is equipped with direction finding radio. By plotting the direction of these stations on the chart, the intersection of the lines drawn to them shows the airplane's position.

The third method is for the airplane to send out signals which are received by two or more ground stations, which then plot the plane's position and tell it by means of radio where it is. The usual course of the airplane equipped with radio is to call nearby ships or land stations and by the intensity of the sound of the responses in the telephone receiver its approximate location can be told.

Not only is radio navigation being used almost entirely by aircraft flying long distances, but also by ships on the sea, as it is surer and more accurate than the old methods. Celestial navigation will not work in heavy fogs, rains, snow or storms, whereas radio navigation will work under practically all conditions. In the not far distant future, radio compass stations to give the position and direction to all aircraft and seacraft will be established in the

Atlantic Ocean on the west coast of Ireland, on the Island of Newfoundland, the south end of Greenland, the tip end of Spain at Cape Finisterre, on the island of San Domingo and in the Canary Islands. These will give a complete control system for the north Atlantic. A similar system could be installed in the Pacific, but for air traffic from America to Asia this will not be necessary as an overland airway can be established straight from our centers of population, such as Chicago and New York, by way of Alaska, through Siberia to Peking and other points in Asia.

Where airways are established, no real navigation is necessary. An airway is very much like a street with markers at every corner telling the names of the cross streets, and with traffic signals to show whether to go or stop. No map is required, not even a knowledge of the country. An aviator rises from a field, sees an arrow on the ground pointing in the direction he wishes to go. Buildings, fields or hills within easy visual distances contain other arrows indicating direction, and he follows these to his destination.

There are airplane instruments which show the ground speed as compared to air speed, and which indicate the drift of an airplane if a cross wind is blowing it sideways. But all these methods of esti-

SKYWAYS

mating one's position in the air are rapidly giving way in the case of pilotage to the established airway with unmistakable marks which can be seen either day or night whenever there is visibility, or to navigation by means of the radio when crossing large water areas or going through storms or clouds.

CHAPTER XI

HOW THE SURFACE OF THE EARTH LOOKS FROM THE AIR

LOOKING at the earth from aircraft gives us a different perspective from anything we have had before. When we first leave the ground, we have an appreciation of great speed, something like that experienced in a fast automobile, except that there are no bumps. At first we see houses, trees, hills and mountains very much as they would look from the top story of a high building, or a mountain. But as we ascend, the heights begin to melt into an apparently flat surface, and the country takes on the appearance of a map. At the height of one mile on a clear day, we are able to see 96 miles in any direction, that is, the airplane is in the center of a visual circle whose diameter is almost 200 miles.

As we continue to ascend, the atmosphere becomes clearer and the sky above us a more intense blue. At 20,000 feet, it seems as though one were suspended in space. One experiences a more profound sensation of solitude in an airplane at high altitudes than any other places, whether in a submarine under the sea, in the midst of a dense forest, out on the desert or deep down in a mine.

It is not a feeling of inferiority but of conscious mastery, as everything is spread out beneath one. At 20,000 feet, one may easily glide an airplane without an engine for twenty miles or more in still air. On a clear day at this height the prominent objects such as cities, rivers, lakes and forests are very easily distinguished, but above that height without the aid of glasses they seem to merge into each other. The sky keeps its intense blue, the air becomes very cold but clear. Great mountains and volcanoes look like little hillocks on a relief map.

When flying near snow clad mountains in the early morning, one may observe the most beautiful color effects. As the plane descends, the dawn light reflected on the snow shifts from bright red, through shades of rose, gradually fading off into pink and white. The immense shadows cast by the high peaks contract as the sun mounts higher.

If it is late afternoon and the sun is up an hour or two on the horizon when the plane is at 20,000 feet, everything will be entirely dark when one reaches the ground. Coming down, we plunge through a swift succession of sunset, twilight and darkness.

When one flies across country toward the west, the day is much longer, and conversely when flying eastward, the day is correspondingly shorter.

THE EARTH FROM THE AIR

At the Equator, the surface of the earth is spinning under the sun at the rate of 1000 miles per hour from west to east. In the Temperate Zone, the rate of speed is only about half this. If an airplane could travel 500 miles an hour, at the latitude of New York it would be in constant daylight flying west.

From his vantage point on high, the airman can see everything that lies on the surface of the ground or water. Nothing that floats on the water can be hidden because there is no such thing as a tree or ditch or overhanging cliff by which it might be concealed.

While a pilot can see all these things, his mind is not capable of recording everything at once, but a photographic plate in a camera can do this. Aerial photography has become the greatest means ever known of mapping a country and finding out what it contains. Soil surveys for agricultural purposes are made from aircraft by photographing the vegetation and deducing from the nature of the growth what sort of plants can best be grown there. Aerial photography has taken the place of the old "cruiser" through the timber lands. Formerly a man had to go through these forests with a pack on his back and would require months to find out the kind and quantity of timber in a certain area. Now the aerial camera photographs the forest in an hour or so, and it can be told with accuracy just what is there. Surveys for minerals and oil are made from the air and the character of rock and stone can be told from photographs. Roads, canals, electric power lines and railways that it used to take months and even years to survey, may be reconnoitered and photographed from aircraft in a short time. Forest fires may be detected from airplanes long before any other means could find them. The condition of cattle on the range and of crops in the fields can be determined from aircraft, for instance if a field of cotton is infested with the boll-weevil.

I once took my friend, Senator Rice, of Hawaii, over one of his sugar plantations where thousands of acres of cane were standing. It was irrigated by ditches and there was almost no way of telling whether these ditches were feeding water into the middle of the great fields or whether they had been clogged up. From our plane, we plainly saw that several feeder ditches a couple of miles inside one of the big fields had stopped working. He immediately sent a gang of men in to repair them, thereby saving thousands of dollars.

In the United States, only about forty percent of our whole area has been accurately mapped. With airplane photography we could map the

Airplanes Are Used in Patrolling Forests to Guard Against Fires

Airplane "Dusting" an Orchard to Prevent Insects from Attacking Trees

whole area for about one-tenth of the cost by old methods, and with much more accuracy.

From a military standpoint, the aerial camera is most important as it will show exactly what the enemy has in certain areas, and what has been the effect of attacks on a locality.

Cameras for aerial work are much like those used on the ground except that they are especially constructed for use at distances of many miles. The lens of the camera has a certain angular displacement, that is, it will take a picture of a certain width at a given distance from the object. If at the height of a mile it photographs an area a mile wide, at two miles it will take in a two mile area, and so on. By noting the altimeter in the plane, one can tell how much territory the photograph will include at any one time.

In the beginning we took photographs by having the camera, of a comparatively long focal length, equipped with sights like a machine gun. An observer pointed the camera at the object to be photographed, sprung the shutter, changed his plate, and then repeated the process. We soon found this was too slow. It gave pretty pictures but they were not accurate enough for mapping purposes. We found it was necessary to hold the camera in an exactly vertical position, which was done by swinging the camera and using a pendulum to make it vertical. Later gyroscopes were used for this same purpose which gave absolute accuracy.

These photographs were examined minutely with magnifying glasses and we learned that a great many things we did not see were contained on the photographic plate. This caused the training of a whole new group of men to do photographic interpretation. They became expert in picking out objects on the aerial photograph that the ordinary untrained person could not identify.

Cameras which work automatically by the use of electricity have come into general use. Glass plates were used at first, arranged for exposure like the leaves of a book. As soon as the exposure was made on one plate, another would slide in and take its place. All the photographs overlapped a little so there would be no doubt that the area to be photographed was completely covered. We used glass plates because we could not make the celluloid film lie perfectly flat. Any little change in its surface would mean a corresponding change on the photograph of the ground. Cameras have now been devised which by the use of air pressure on the back of the celluloid film keep it perfectly flat.

An airplane, no matter in what position it may be flying, up, down or horizontally, can take pictures of an area and the camera will record the altitude, speed and direction at which the plane is flying. In other words, with a modern camera, the pilot can take off, start his camera going and fly anywhere he desires, then when he returns and the film is developed, it will give an accurate record of where he has been, and may be put into a map.

This map will show not only the objects on the ground, but also the elevations, depressions, hills, valleys and mountains. This vertical control has been brought about by using several lenses at the same time, set at different fixed angles. The altitude of the airplane is known and from these two factors the height of mountains and undulations in the ground can be figured out, and these calculations embodied in a map which will be accurate in all details.

The aerial camera has nowhere near reached its ultimate development. When I was in Germany two years ago, I was shown a camera which would take photographs in the air as it went along, develop them automatically and transmit the photographs by radio to a station on the ground.

An instrument utilizing the photographic plate has been devised which employs a map of the country as a background, and will show the direction in which the airplane is flying, its speed and altitude as well. The pilot can look at this record and see exactly where he is, irrespective of whether he can see the ground or not. If there is any doubt about his position, he can get cross bearings from radio compass stations. This is the way that aerial bombardment and attacks on distant places will be made in the future.

Cloud forms are extremely interesting. The billowy masses of cumulus clouds, or thunder-heads, contain aerial mountains, valleys and canyons. They appear to be so massive and solid that we could almost land on them. I have often practiced a "falling leaf" landing on the top of a cloud and believe after many trials that I could land an airplane on the ground from a falling leaf, but the risk was so great that I never actually tried it. One of the most thrilling things in the air is to fly up the great valleys and canyons of these white clouds. As the sun shines through them, all the colors of the rainbow are seen. If the shadow of the airplane is projected on the side of a cloud, this image will always be surrounded by a rainbow, because the light reflected off the outer edges of the plane strikes the particles of water in the clouds so as to make prisms of them and they break the beam up into the colors of the spectrum.

The appearance of rain, hail, snow or sleet when

THE EARTH FROM THE AIR

one is flying in the air is entirely different than when viewed from the ground. Inside a cloud containing snow or sleet, it is almost pitch dark. Sometimes low lying fogs or clouds cover the lower stories of the houses of a city, letting the church steeples and high towers stick up through them. This condition is often encountered when flying over mountain ranges, the valleys and lower altitudes cannot be seen but the high peaks and glistening glaciers lie in the clear sunlight.

All great cities have a distinctive atmosphere over them, depending on the leading industry conducted there. Where a great deal of coal is used, there is a lot of fixed carbon in the air which goes up thousands of feet. For instance, as one approaches Pittsburgh from afar off a pall of smoke may be seen quite distinctly, rising high in the air and extending up and down the Monongahela Valley for perhaps a hundred miles. Over Pittsburgh, the aviator can taste and smell the sulphur from the coke ovens. A great many chemicals are contained in the atmosphere over any large city, due to the combustion of different materials. The air over Chicago has its own unique character, due to the presence of the stockyards where a great deal of animal matter is burned. New York is dissimilar to Philadelphia or Boston. It is difficult to explain just what this difference is, but it is quite evident to the pilot whose sense of taste and smell has not been dulled by the use of tobacco.

Man has always striven for the vantage point which altitude gives to the eye. Never in our history have we been able to see as much or learn as much of the earth's surface as we do from aircraft.

CHAPTER XII

AIRPLANE MANEUVERS

An airplane has to be maneuvered in the air just as an automobile has to be driven, turned and handled on the ground, or a horse made to do his different movements, changes of direction, jumps and stops. The difference between an airplane and anything on the ground is that the plane has three dimensions to move in, up, down and across. It is entirely immersed in a fluid in which it can fly right side up, on its side or it can turn over on its back and fly upside down.

Certain simple maneuvers are necessary in flying any airplane. When it leaves the ground, the pilot must place it so that its tail will rise and it will be in line of flight, then he must climb it, turn it to right or left, glide it toward the earth and when approaching the ground, bring it to a horizontal position and allow it to sink to its landing.

All airplanes are constructed so they are heavier in front than behind, and they will fall on the "nose" or in a forward direction. An airplane cannot slip back. It may fall backward for a little way but will gradually come down with its nose pointed toward the ground. All pilots should be taught how to bring a plane out of a spin. In teaching this, the plane is climbed to a safe height, the motor shut off and the nose pointed straight up. When a pilot goes into his first stall, he experiences a sensation entirely different from anything he ever felt before. All speed or forward motion ceases, the engine is silent, there is no whistling of wind through the wires or along the wings. The airplane comes to complete rest and for a moment one feels suspended in space way above the earth. Then it slips over, falling off on one wing and will go into a spin, which is more or less rapid according to the construction of the airplane. It is not necessary for the engine of an airplane to stop to produce a stall. If the airplane is inclined upward at an angle which makes it impossible for the engine to continue to pull the airplane through the air, it will stall; or if the engine is throttled to a diminished speed and put at too great an angle of ascent, the same result will ensue.

No engine is powerful enough to pull an airplane straight out of a stall, once the plane has come to rest in the air, that is, lost its forward motion. The controls should be put on neutral, the rudder, elevator and ailerons being held exactly in the center. In a few moments, the airplane has attained sufficient speed so the controls will act and the plane

AIRPLANE MANEUVERS
can be pulled out into normal flying position. One must have an altitude of over 300 feet to recover from a stall.

The experienced pilot with sensitive reflexes can feel a stall coming. He knows, when his airplane begins to "mush" and he senses the laboring of his propellor, that he must act quickly to avert it. The ailerons or controls on the tips of the wings are the first to be affected. If he tries to incline his airplane from side to side, there is no response. Next the elevator becomes inoperative, and last the rudder. By that time the airplane is nearly ready to fall. These things often come with the greatest rapidity and all at once. Instant action, almost automatic, on the part of the pilot is necessary to prevent the stall.

If the control surfaces are very large and push against the air a great deal, as was the case with some of the old types, the plane may be held in a stall for a long way. Some airplanes may be constructed in a faulty manner, making it impossible to pull them out. Every machine has to be tested for that purpose by the test pilots, who put them into every attitude and then bring them out again. Before the days of parachutes, fatalities among test pilots were common and frequent, but now they can usually extricate themselves.

Maneuvers in the air are a source of great interest and amazement to spectators, and a group of aviators has grown up, called "Gypsy pilots" who make their living by giving exhibitions and stunts. If both the airplanes and pilots are in good condition, there is no great danger in stunt flying, a stunt being considered a more or less difficult maneuver which would not be necessary in ordinary flying.

The ordinary commercial pilot needs to know comparatively few maneuvers, but a pilot trained for war in the air must know them all. Combat between two individuals in the best single seater pursuit planes is the greatest test of human ingenuity and lightning judgment possible. After the men recognize each other as enemies, each strives to approach the other from above, and if the sun is shining, to be between the sun and their opponent, so that he gets the sun's rays full in the face and can only see with difficulty. They spar for openings like boxers or wrestlers. The adversary is made to turn to the left and right, and instant notation is made of how he does it the quickest. When one thinks he has found a weak point in the other, he rushes in with lightning speed to take advantage of it. The adversary tries to parry this with a maneuver which will give him the advantage. If a pilot does not

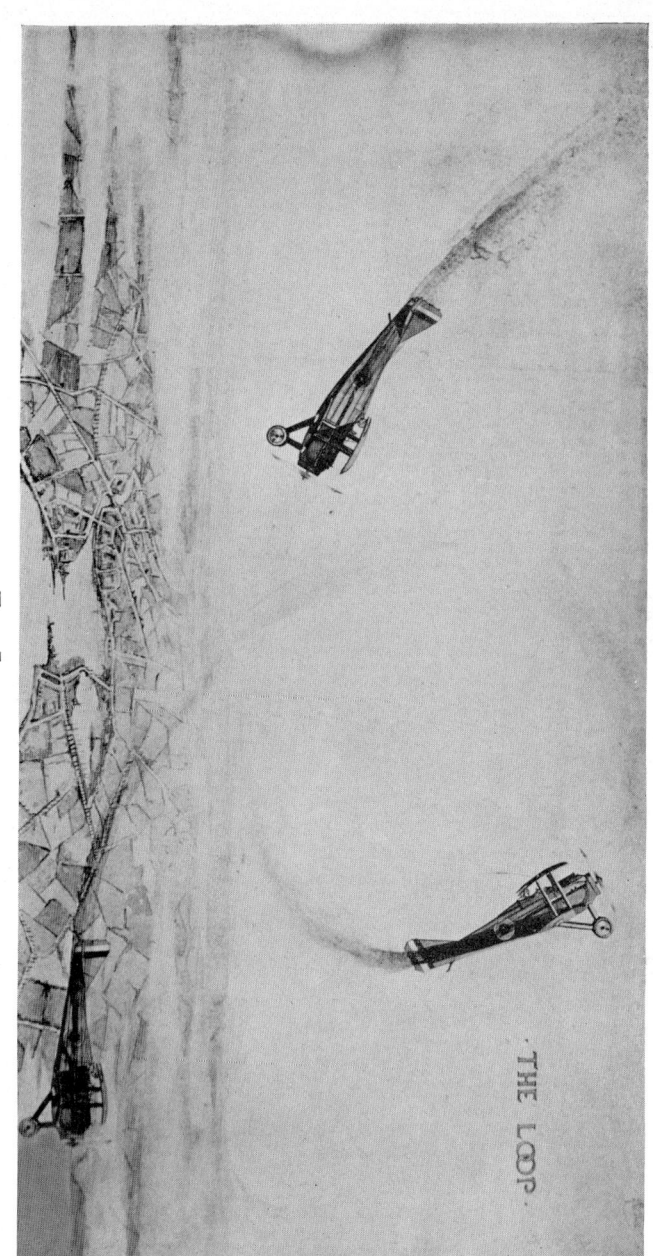
The Loop

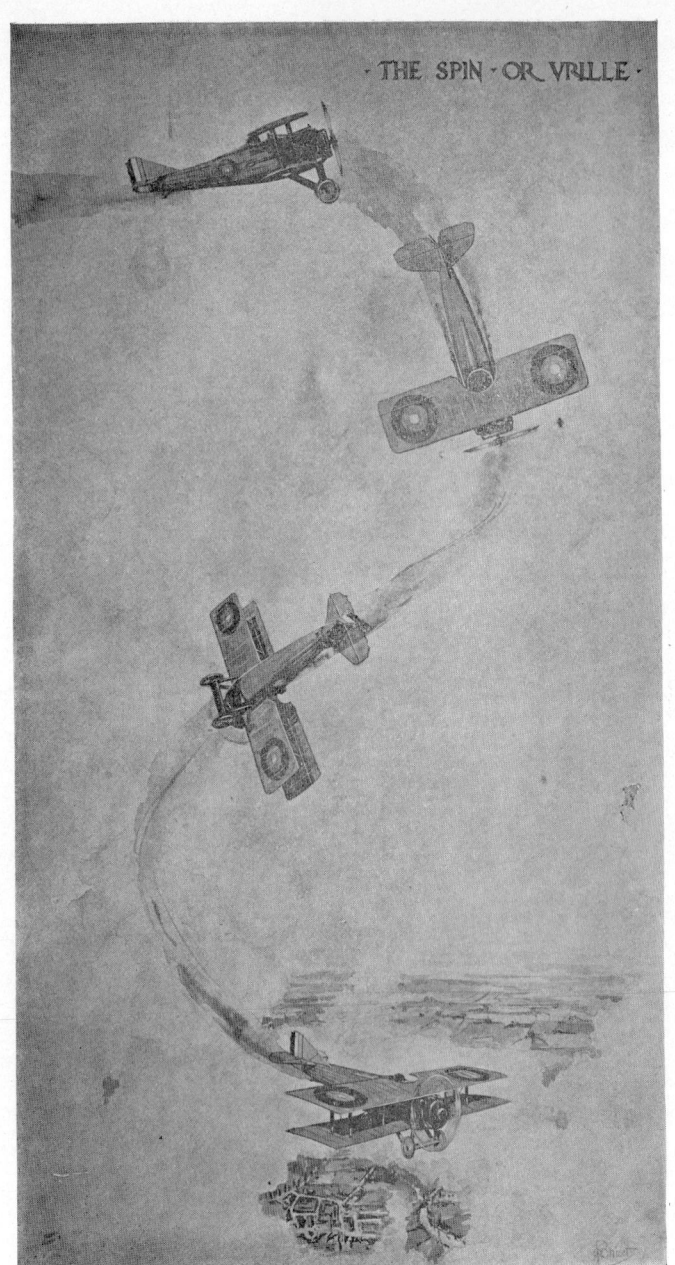

The Spin or Vrille

AIRPLANE MANEUVERS

know every maneuver his airplane is capable of, he is sure to meet death and fail in his military mission.

One of the ordinary maneuvers is "looping." An inside loop is one in which the airplane is headed down until sufficient speed is obtained, then the controls are pulled back until the plane describes a complete circle, at the top of which the plane is upside down. With the high powered engines of today, this is a simple maneuver. Centrifugal force keeps the pilot down in his seat. A properly executed loop would not even require that the pilot be held in with a belt, although at one instant he would be upside down.

A similar maneuver, called an outside loop, can be made in the opposite direction. Instead of pulling the airplane upward, it is pushed over forward, and one is upside down at the bottom of the circle. In this case, the centrifugal force acts in the opposite way and the pilot must be securely strapped in the plane, otherwise he will be thrown out.

A pilot often experiences the sensation of the airplane falling away under him, that is, the airplane is going faster than he is and his belt pulls him forward. The Spad airplanes we had during the war dived very rapidly and always fell away from the pilot, whereas the Nieuports began their dive slowly because they were very light and had broad rotary motors. They acted in just the opposite way, the pilot would fall forward in the belt when he began a straight dive.

In a real dive, one goes in a perfectly perpendicular direction for the ground, with the motor full on. This is seldom seen in time of peace because the strain on the structure of the plane is so great that a wing is very apt to be lost. Most of the maneuvers called "dives" during peace time are merely glides at a steep angle.

The Immelmann Turn is an important maneuver, as it enables one to reverse the direction of flight with the greatest rapidity. In air fighting, the ordinary bank turn was found to be too slow, and a German named Immelmann devised a maneuver which depended on pulling the airplane upward with the elevator and then when it assumed a vertical position, kicking it over sideways with the rudder bar, which brought the nose of the airplane into the opposite direction without losing altitude.

Another spectacular maneuver is the barrel roll, where the airplane is turned over and over sideways while in horizontal flight. In other words, the plane is spun about a horizontal axis instead of a vertical axis.

One of the most difficult and beautiful maneuvers, which has no particularly practical application

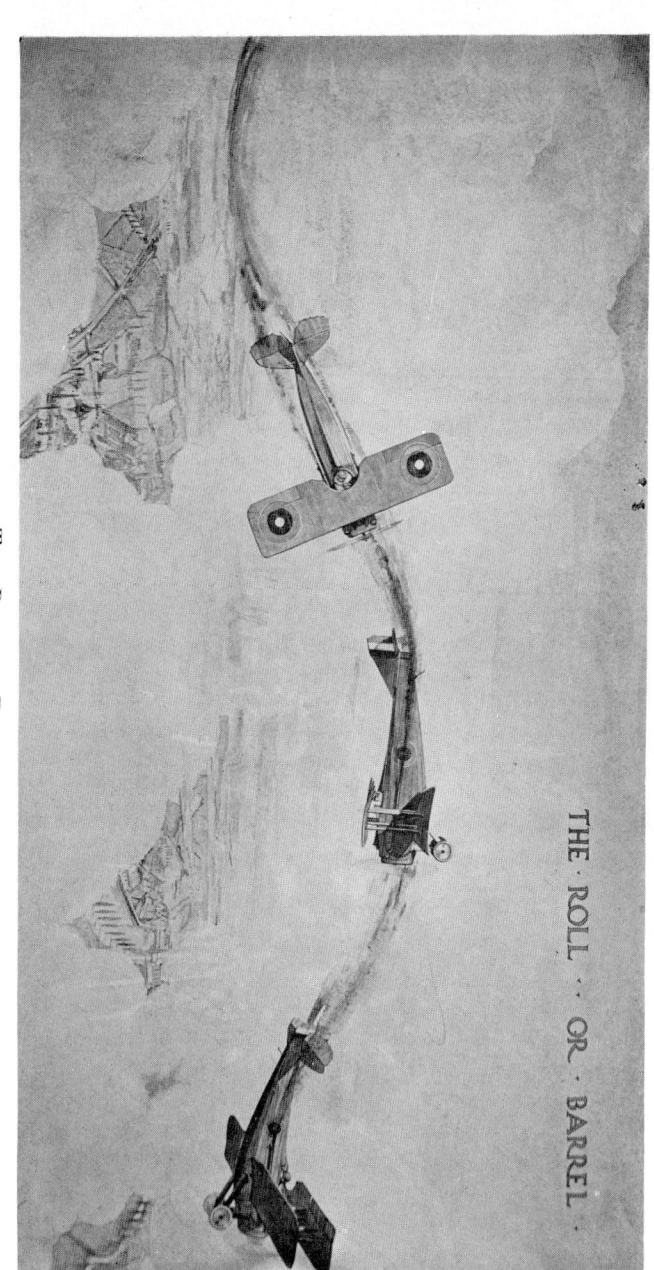

The Roll or Barrel

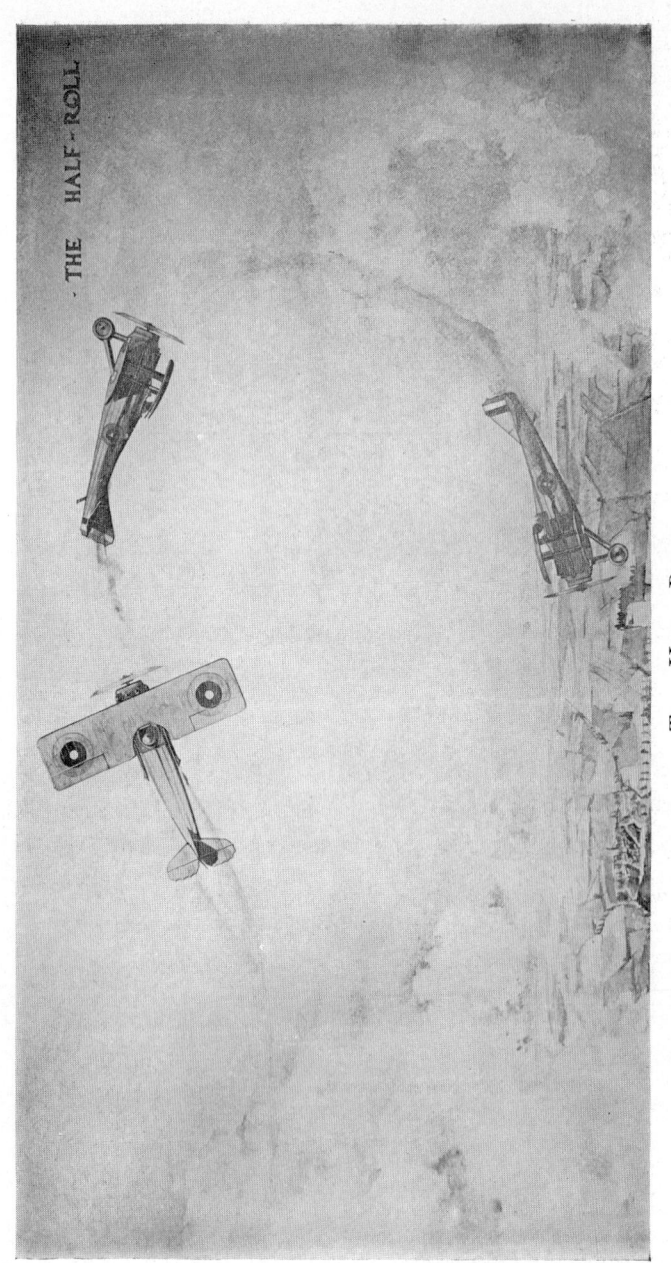

The Half Roll

AIRPLANE MANEUVERS

except to teach the pilot an exquisite sense of balance, is known as the "falling leaf." A good falling leaf is seldom seen. To execute it, the airplane is put just into the first part of a stall with its right wing up and left wing low. As it falls to the left, the pilot maintains just enough speed to throw the left wing up and the right one down when the process is reversed to the right. An expert pilot can bring an airplane almost straight down by this maneuver, and landings have actually been made from it.

There are only a few basic maneuvers, such as bank turns, spirals, side slips, stalls, spins, rolls, Immelmann turns, sharp dives and zooms. Many times one may be combined with another for a useful purpose. A pilot with resourcefulness and ability is always able to apply maneuvers in a new way, or to devise others. With the war flyer this is absolutely essential, and the commercial flyer must know enough so he will be able to extricate his airplane from a dangerous position into which it may be placed by storms, currents of air, motor stoppage or the breaking or jamming of some control. For instance, on taking off he may break a wheel or both wheels. If a good body of water is nearby, it is better to land in it under these conditions. With one wheel off, if a very slow landing is made with the airplane inclined slightly toward the good wheel, a normal landing can often be effected. If both wheels are gone and a slow landing is made, either the pieces of the landing gear will be broken off and the plane slide along on its bottom, or it may turn over slowly. If landed too fast, the plane will invariably turn over and crack up.

The motor may suddenly cut out when the pilot is over a dense forest. In such cases, airplanes have been brought in with minimum speed and practically stalled just as they hit the tops of the trees. The cushion effect of the wings hitting the limbs of trees and letting the airplane down gradually is often sufficient to save the occupants. If a forest is rather open, with trees ten or twelve feet apart, and a glide can be made into it along the side, it is not a particularly dangerous undertaking. The airplane may be directed between two trees from ten to twenty feet apart, which will smash off both wings, and if the fuselage of the plane is within ten or twenty feet of the ground, it will go ahead without any serious smash as practically all the speed will have been taken out of it.

A forced landing in mountains confronts the pilot with another test of judgment. Again every advantage must be taken of the circumstances. If there are any fields or clear spaces on the mountain side, the plane may be directed with considerable

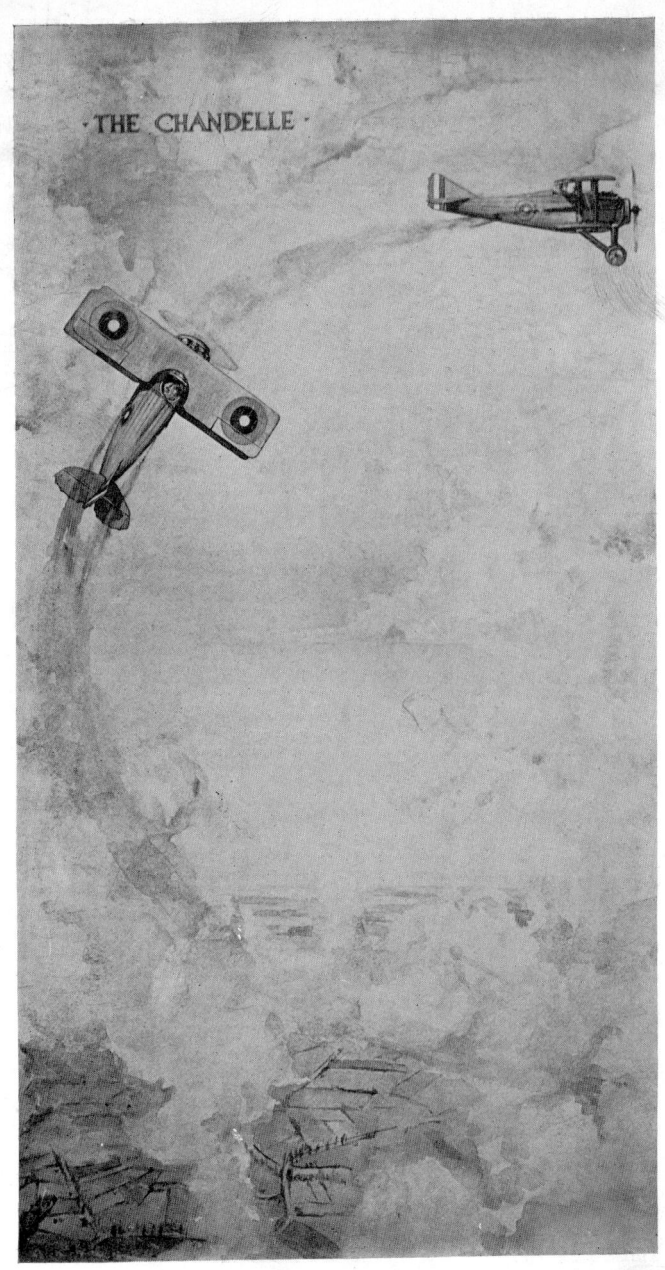

The Chandelle

The Renversement

AIRPLANE MANEUVERS

speed to their lowest point, then turned uphill when within a few feet of the ground. In this way, it will lose speed more rapidly than if it were flying on the level. To attempt a landing in the mountains downhill is a very dangerous undertaking. If a landing has to be made into the face of a cliff or vertical canyon, the plane should be directed straight toward it at its minimum speed, and just before the instant of impact, swung sharply to one side and the crash taken out on the end of a wing. In this way the shock will be deadened and the danger of fire minimized as the airplane will not hit on its nose. I have seen one instance of this kind of landing, both the pilot and observer escaping without serious injury.

Always, landings must be made with the minimum speed when the airplane touches the ground, and it is the ability to judge the difference between stalling speed and the minimum safe flying speed that makes a good pilot. A man may be an excellent pilot in the air but a very poor one near the ground.

Just after we returned to the United States from the European war, most of the flying men were quite dubious about safe flying across the Allegheny or Rocky Mountains. They feared it would be impossible to land with safety in this rough country. One day I took a single-seater airplane, an SE5, containing only enough gas for one and three-quarter hours' flying, and started out from Bolling Field accompanied by three of the best pilots in the United States, in two-seater DH airplanes, which carried sufficient gas for three hours' flying. From Washington we headed toward the Allegheny Mountains for Dayton, Ohio. Encountering a heavy head wind as I left the Capital, I began to run out of gas when over the Blue Ridge Mountains and determined on landing. I had arranged a signal with Col. Hartney that he would take command of the three airplanes when I decided to land.

So rough was the country that it took me twenty minutes to find a place to go down, on a side hill covered with large rocks. I landed and spread a cloth on the ground which I had carried for the purpose, to indicate where the other planes should place their wheels upon coming down. Each pilot was an expert in his own method of landing.

Col. Hartney approached the landing point first, side-slipping, that is, letting the airplane lose altitude by tilting it up on its side and allowing it to slide, keeping perfect control all the way. A side-slip to a landing is one of the best methods of bringing an airplane in, as there is less chance for stalling if the pilot knows his business. Col. Hartney landed exactly on the mark.

Next to come in was Lieut. Logan, one of the greatest pilots that ever lived. He glided with considerable speed for the mark and when approaching it, swung his airplane from side to side, "fishtailing," that is, exposing the flat side of the plane's body to the air so as to kill his speed. He also landed on the panel.

The third to land was Major Ocker. He made a very flat slow glide, keeping himself in the air with his engine. As he would approach stalling speed, he would give the airplane a little more engine and pull it out, and then repeat the process. He also landed with minimum speed on the cloth.

Here were three entirely different ways of bringing an airplane in, made by leaders in the art of aviation. Each was good and according to the particular temperament of the man making it. While certain rules cannot be transgressed without sure death in the air, a great deal of art is required in a finished pilot. We made several other landings on this trip, in the heart of the mountains, showing that we could get in and out of almost any place required.

A forced landing in a fog is one of the worst contingencies that a pilot has to face. Nothing is visible in the direction of the earth. An airplane is kept on an even keel only by the use of instruments. If the pilot is not equipped with a parachute, he must remain with the airplane and the only thing he can do is to let his plane glide down with the minimum speed until the inevitable crash comes. He should let all the gasoline out of his gas tanks, and put some sort of pad in front of his head and chest—coats, clothing, seats or anything that is soft. He should remove his flying glasses and keep his head as near the pad as possible, so that it will not have a long way to swing when it hits. If the airplane comes down slowly in this way, a pilot has more than an even chance to get away with a landing. But under these conditions, it is extremely difficult not to stall and fall to the earth out of control. Nowadays, when everybody is equipped with a parachute, most pilots jump out when their engine stops or they are forced to land in a fog. Usually a drop of ninety feet is necessary before the chute opens, but if the airplane is going at very high speed, around two hundred miles an hour for instance, the chute will open in less distance than this. Usually two or three swings from side to side are made by the body of the pilot after the parachute begins to spread out in the air, and it is seldom that a man can land safely before the third swing is made. However, I have seen one instance in which a pilot jumped out of his airplane apparently within one hundred feet of the ground, and struck it on the second swing. He was uninjured except for a sprained ankle.

Landing in deep snow is not a difficult matter. It should be done in the same way as landing on water. The ordinary wheeled airplane is able to take off or land in eighteen inches or even two feet of snow if it is not too wet. Anything deeper than that requires skis or special landing gear.

If the pilot must land in soft or muddy ground, he should be especially careful to come in at minimum speed. Often on encountering mud, the tail of the plane starts to go up, but a good blast on the propellor will direct a stream of air back on the stabilizer which will hold the tail down. In getting out of muddy places, the wheels will frequently throw large pieces of mud against the propellor which may break it. This can be counteracted by smearing the wheels with heavy oil or axle grease to prevent their picking up mud.

CHAPTER XIII

AIRSHIPS

NOT only during the war, but since, the airship has demonstrated its great potentialities. The German airship, Graf Zeppelin, completely circumnavigated the globe, starting from Friedrichshafen and proceeding to Tokyo, Japan, thence to San Diego, California, to Lakehurst, New Jersey, and back to its home port. It carried passengers, mail and express and made the trip on schedule time. It purposely encountered or avoided storms, high winds and extremes of temperature.

The airship, as distinguished from the airplane, depends for its sustentation on being filled with a gas that is lighter than air. This causes it to float in the air like a boat does on the water. It is a descendant of the balloon, much as the airplane is a descendant of the kite. Balloons were used by the ancients, the envelopes being made of various light materials, filled with heated air. Usually a fire was made and when the smoke had disappeared and only the hot embers remained, the envelope of the balloon was brought over the fire. (When mixed with smoke, the air is heavier.) When a sufficient amount of heated air had gone into the balloon, judged by the pull it gave on the ropes holding it, it was released and went up until the hot air cooled, then it came down. Other hot air balloons were made that carried with them fires suspended underneath, consequently they stayed up longer. Many Fourth of July balloons are made like that today.

After awhile, men ascended in hot air balloons and jumped out in parachutes before the balloons collapsed. Sometimes as they ascended they held on to a bar suspended under the balloon and performed various acrobatic feats for the edification of crowds at country fairs.

About 150 years ago, it was found that hydrogen gas would lift a balloon. This was put to practical use during the French Revolution in 1789 while Paris was besieged, when balloons with messages were sent out of the city. The pilot took with him some carrier pigeons, which he released and sent back with messages to the besieged fortress.

The free hydrogen balloon gave us a great deal of information about weather conditions and about the action of gases as a supporting medium for lighter-than-air craft. There is a tremendous rush of air around an airplane as it flies through the atmosphere, but when a free balloon leaves the ground, it floats along in the wind and at the same speed as the wind. Everything is perfectly still to the occupants of the basket. Sounds from the earth, such as people talking or dogs barking, can be heard very distinctly from great heights.

The free balloon has also revealed a great deal about up and down currents of air, which are due to the sun warming the atmosphere. At the same time, the heat of the sun expands the gas in the balloon, causing it to rise rapidly as it displaces more air. Conversely, when the air cools in the afternoon, down currents are created and the gas is contracted, which makes the balloon go down. This necessitates the use of ballast, in the form of sand, water or other substances that can easily be let out to lighten it. In this way, equilibrium can be maintained for a time.

Early experiments showed that if a balloon ascended to great heights, the atmospheric pressure on the envelope was reduced and the hydrogen gas would expand and might burst the envelope. Consequently, a balloon of a certain size, filled with a certain amount of gas, would have to be held within certain limits of altitude, otherwise it would explode. Valves were invented for expelling gas quickly in an emergency, so as to halt a too rapid rise of the balloon. A means for landing was worked out and anchors, drag ropes and parachutes became standard equipment. Later, altimeters and radio were used.

Free balloons were entirely at the mercy of the elements and were sometimes swept into storms and lost. In the few cases where the aeronauts survived, they gave us remarkable accounts of how storms behaved in their centers, which were not always believed at the time, but which have since been proved to be accurate.

The next step was to make these balloons dirigible, that is, to go where their occupants desired. There were many attempts at this, some taking the form of oars which were actuated by hand; propellors were tried, actuated by compressed air and tubes and springs; even steam engines were experimented with. It was soon found that the oval balloon with the basket suspension was not suitable for this kind of use. When the basket was impelled forward at any speed, the envelope would be blown inward by the pressure of the air from whatever direction the balloon was going. This would distort the envelope, force gas out of it and the balloon would descend. An interior ballonet, or section of balloon, was then invented, into which air could be pumped either by pressure of the air itself or by an auxiliary air fan. The stronger the wind blew, the more air could be put into the ballonet.

In this way, the envelope of the balloon could be maintained in its original form.

Military captive balloons were quick to avail themselves of this invention. Napoleon took balloons with him to Egypt in 1803. We used them in our Civil War, and it was with Professor Lowe, who handled balloons for General McClelland's army in 1862 that Count Zeppelin had the first experience in balloons.

About the time of the advent of the gasoline engine in 1879, the shape of captive balloons had changed from the old spherical type to a streamline form almost egg shaped, with fins or stabilizers to keep them from swaying in the wind, and with wind chutes which admitted the air into the auxiliary ballonet. These balloons were developed so they could be handled in winds up to forty or fifty miles an hour, and maneuvered at a height of 3000 feet above the ground by their wire cables.

In the nineties, gasoline engines were successfully used with balloons and various flights were made, particularly in France by Santos Dumont, a Brazilian, who won the Deutsch de la Meurthe prizes, the first ones put up for a controlled flight through the air from one point to another and back. The Santos Dumont airships were non-rigid, cigar shaped and had an interior ballonet. The engines were suspended from them, much like the baskets on the old free balloons.

Gradually the dirigible began to take on a keel outside the envelope on which the engines were placed. Then the envelope itself was stiffened by reinforcing the nose with strips of wood or metal so it would hold its shape. After this, instead of filling the whole envelope of the airship with gas, it was divided into sections so that if one part were pierced, or expanded or contracted too greatly, it would not affect the others.

Count Zeppelin in Germany was one of the first to apply his ideas seriously to developing an airship which would be a real air cruiser. He came of a wealthy and prominent family, and had a most distinguished record as a soldier. Before the first successful gasoline engine was built in the seventies, he had made up models of dirigible airships. His first idea was to make the airship in the form of a sausage, with several links one behind the other, under which would be suspended the keel or rigid framework to hold these sections in line. This form was adopted so as to distribute the lifting force of the gas in various receptacles and also to prevent the ship from being ripped in two, in case of striking a line squall. Being flexible, they figured it would withstand the strain.

Throughout the eighties he worked on his ship, which gradually took the form of a rigid envelope, a cigar shaped structure made of wood and metal into which several balloons containing lifting gas were placed. The engines were outside, suspended from the rigid framework. This construction marked a decided advance in lighter-than-air design. Here at once was a rigid framework which could not be destroyed by the action of the wind. The ballonets in the interior of the ship could not only keep their shape, no matter how the wind blew outside, but on account of the air space between them and the envelope, they were protected from sudden changes of temperature.

Problems of stability, keeping the airship on an even keel in all kinds of weather and handling it in storms, required a great deal of experimental and practical work.

When the ship left its hangar, it was loaded with gasoline, fuel for its engines, besides a certain amount of ballast to make up for the expansion and contraction of the lifting gas in the ballonets. When the sun's rays caused the hydrogen to expand, some of it would have to be valved in order to keep the ship from rising too high. When the air cooled in the evening, the gas contracted and the ship would begin to descend, so ballast would

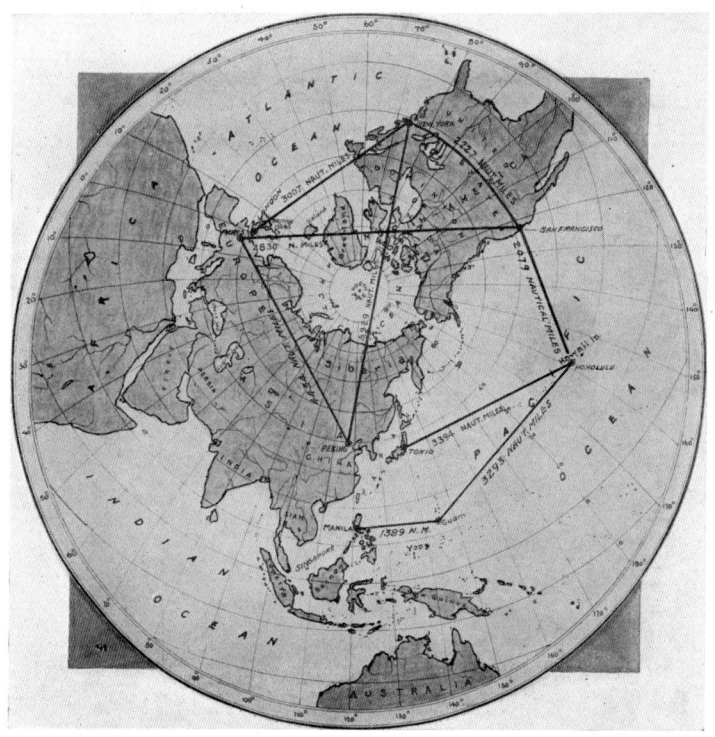

AIRLINE DISTANCE BETWEEN CENTERS OF POPULATION IN THE NORTHERN HEMISPHERE

Mrs. Mitchell, Dr. Eckener, and Captain Lehmann During an Inspection of the Zeppelin Works

have to be thrown out to restore equilibrium. Great care had to be taken in valving the gas and discharging ballast, in order to keep the ship's trim constant. Valving gas out of the top of the airship was a dangerous process, particularly in thunder storms, as hydrogen is easily ignited.

It was found that the long cigar shaped structures, the form of the earliest Zeppelins, were not strong enough to withstand the up and down currents of the air, or the torsion caused by quickly putting the rudder over to one side when making a turn. Among others, the American airship, Shenandoah, was lost in a line squall in 1925. An up and down current of air caught it amidships and tore it in two. The British airship, R-36, was destroyed and its crew lost when the rudders were put hard over, breaking the ship in the middle.

The development of Zeppelin airships was continuous, from the first successful one launched in 1900 until the present Graf Zeppelin which made the round-the-world flight, many parts for which had been designed and provided for by Count Zeppelin himself. This airship embodies many new principles, but even it is a primitive structure compared to what the airship of the future will be. It was made just as thick amidships as the size of the hangars permitted, and would have been made thicker had these been larger. The shape of the ideal airship should approach that of an egg, in which form it will offer hardly more resistance to the air than would a long narrow one.

    The Graf Zeppelin has an envelope entirely different from any of its predecessors. It also has two keels, one on the bottom something like the keel of a steamship, and another running the whole length of the ship, about one third of the way up. To both these keels the metal bars which compose the airship skeleton are securely fastened. Every fourth section is doubly reinforced and a new metal, called electron, which is lighter than duralumin, has been extensively used. Most important of all, a fuel gas is used instead of gasoline. This gas has the same weight as air, so when it is consumed by the motors and air takes its place, there is no change in the weight of the ship. This makes it possible to fill the ballonets only partially full of lifting gas, thus allowing plenty of room for expansion and obviating the necessity of valving gas when it expands. Consequently no overhead valves are provided as in the old ships, and no gas has to be valved during storms. Of course there are emergency valves. But the ordinary loss of gas in this, the newest of the Zeppelins, is only that which leaks out through the goldbeater's skin bags in which it is contained,

Cross Section of the German Airship Graf Zeppelin. The Members and Trusses Are Set Up Flat Then Assembled as Above

Graf Zeppelin Showing the Two Keels, One at the Bottom, One Two-Thirds of the Way Up. The Lower Ballonet Contains the Gas for Fuel, the Upper Contains the Hydrogen Gas Which Lifts the Airship

which is comparable to the ordinary leakage of water into a well-built vessel on the sea. Goldbeater's skin, made from the intestines of cattle, is the most impervious substance obtainable for containing the gas. This use of fuel gas in place of gasoline, by making possible the system of lifting gas compartments which do not have to be touched from one end of the journey to the other, has tremendously increased the airship's cruising radius and safety.

At present, airships are not fast enough. Ordinarily they make from sixty-five to seventy miles an hour in still air. They need over one hundred miles speed in order to successfully "buck" storms or avoid them by going around them; but with modern engines and propellors, this can be easily accomplished.

Non-explosive and non-inflammable gases are beginning to be used instead of hydrogen. Helium, a gas found in combination with coal gas, in certain places, has been quite extensively used. It is 18 percent heavier than hydrogen. It is extracted by cooling the coal gas until it begins to liquefy. Helium has a lower liquefying point, and the helium is drained off from the top of the coal gas and compressed into tubes. Chemists are working on other non-inflammable gases. It may reasonably be hoped that in a short time all airships will be equipped with gas that will not ignite.

The rigid airship, as exemplified by the Zeppelin, has proved itself to be the most practical vehicle for long distance air navigation where a more or less constant altitude can be held and where the envelope is not subject to being covered with ice and sleet. Fog is no impediment to it. It can sail by dead reckoning and radio navigation better than any ship on the sea because its speed is so much greater.

The landing of these great ships around 1000 feet in length presents a great many problems. In ordinary winds up to 30 miles an hour, the mooring mast is a very practical arrangement. These structures are built up to a height of about 200 feet by a system of steel girders. At the top is a cone shaped structure into which the nose of the airship fits. It is provided with rollers and a swivel so that the ship may swing clear around the mast in accordance with the way the wind is blowing. The mooring mast is equipped with an elevator which takes passengers and freight up to the landing stage, and gangways are provided from the mast to the airship so that everything may be put aboard easily. When an airship comes in for a landing, it lowers a cable which is attached to the mooring mast, and the ship pulled directly to its position and held there.

Another system of taking care of airships on the ground is the hangar, a large building one thousand feet or more in length, three or four hundred feet wide, into which the airship can be drawn. Leading out from the hangar are tracks on the ground to which movable cars are attached, usually actuated by cable and a reeling-in device. The airship comes in headed to the wind and drops its mooring ropes which are caught by landing crews and attached to the movable cars, hauled up and the airship is pulled into the hangar.

An airship must be landed head to the wind, for if it is caught sideways by the wind as it enters the hangar, it is very apt to be broken in two, consequently modern airship stations contemplate constructing hangars in the form of a star, so that an airship will always find one entry in suitable position to enter head to the wind. These hangars have doors at each end, and in the middle of the series of hangars a turn-table is provided so that the airship may be pulled in to the center and turned in any direction desired, so that when it goes out, it can be placed head to the wind.

Another form of mooring contemplated is a sort of nest construction into which the lower part of the ship fits. This nest could be turned clear around the circumference so it would always be head to the wind. The ship would be placed in this nest similar to the way it is put into a hangar. Those who favor the nacelle in place of the mooring mast point out that the danger to an airship moored to a mast is from the waves of air that come under it and whip it up and down. If these become severe enough, the airship will be torn to pieces, whereas in a nacelle, the air cannot get under it, and it is therefore secure.

Naturally a great deal of development will take place in proper ports for airships. While the initial equipment is somewhat expensive, it cannot compare with the expense incident to the construction and operation of railroads. The cost per passenger mile in airship travel is also much less than that of an airplane or even a railroad, and apparently will be only slightly more than that of a fast steamer.

New uses and opportunities for airships are constantly presenting themselves. For one thing, airplanes can land on airships. We accomplished this for the first time in the United States in 1922. After a series of experiments lasting over a couple of years, we equipped a small non-rigid airship with a hooking on device for airplanes. Flying along at

Glider or Motorless Flying Machine Attached to an Airplane, in This Case Used as a Target, but Larger Ones May Be Used for Landing Passengers from Airplanes

Cabin of an Airship with a Device for Carrying Airplane Underneath

a speed of sixty-five miles an hour, the airplane came up under it and hooked on without trouble. Then the plane took off from the ship with no apparent change in the ship's specific gravity. This is largely due to the fact that the speed at which the airship goes makes the airplane practically hold itself up by its own wings. Also it was found that by running up the airplane's propellor, more speed could be given to the airship.

This means that passengers, freight and fuel can be delivered by airplanes to airships passing over. In war, airplanes can be carried by airships any place over the sea or land, and launched. By directional radio they can find their way back to the airship and be refueled. I had plans and specifications drawn up for airships that would carry one squadron of twenty-four airplanes. A ship like this could cross the Atlantic or Pacific and return without refueling. Each airplane could carry plenty of ammunition, fuel, spare parts and even extra personnel for a considerable campaign. An airship as an airplane carrier over the sea is far superior to an airplane carrier in the form of a ship on the water, and only costs a fraction as much.

An airship can carry aerial torpedoes which may be launched and guided by radio for hundreds of miles. It can carry gliding bombs, which are equipped with wings. When dropped, they take up flight as soon as sufficient speed is obtained, guided by the gyroscopic rudder. During the war, airships were equipped with baskets which could be let down a couple of thousand feet, with observers in them. The airship could stay above a strata of cloud, hidden from troops on the ground, while the observers saw everything that was going on and communicated with the ship by telephone.

Airship travel is very comfortable. There is plenty of room and good beds to sleep in. Food can be prepared as conveniently as on seacraft. The cabins can be heated and every comfort provided for.

CHAPTER XIV

THE SPORTING SIDE OF AVIATION

THE word "sport" is used to cover a multitude of things—and sins, for that matter. A sportsman may be defined as "one who competes fairly and squarely in any contest according to the unwritten rules and spirit of fair play." A well-developed sporting spirit makes a better man in any walk of life, whether in business, a profession, or in sports themselves.

In all sports there is the element of hazard, but in none of them does it enter to the same extent as in the sporting side of aviation. I have indulged in most of the present-day sports, but the thrill and interest of work in the air places it among the first.

I have never asked anyone to go in the air with me. Of course, in the Army, when it was a matter of duty for a person to accompany me, orders were issued, but otherwise the request has always come from the other party. I remember one occurrence just after my return from the World War, which illustrates one phase of aviation's sporting side. A number of the older Army officers had taken flying training and been given their flying ratings, when as a matter of fact they were only able to hobble off the ground in a horizontal position with their training planes, and then about half fly back and "mush" down on the field again. After having once accomplished this feat they were decorated with the aviator's wings—a precious thing to the flying man. After that, they always took one of the best pilots with them to handle the plane whenever they went in the air, carefully refraining from touching the controls. It was not that they did not want to fly, but they just could not master the art. They didn't know what it was all about when we discussed rapid maneuvers in the air and their effect on one's sense of balance, perception, judgment and vision and— what was even more marked—their effect on one's stomach. Two of them asked me to take them up and show them what we meant. I was particularly glad to do it, as a new American two-seater airplane had just been delivered to me which was designed to stand the strains of strenuous maneuvers. I started up with the first officer, climbing to about 6000 feet, where I dived the airplane vertically with the full motor. Our terminal velocity was around 250 to 300 miles an hour. Whipping the airplane out of this, I shot it straight up on its tail for about 1000 feet, where I held it until it went into a stall. It fell off on a wing and went into a spin, from which I extricated it in a few moments, when I saw that my companion was somewhat flustered. As I took up level flight he signaled me that he had had enough, and I landed. His head was completely in a whirl and he could hear nothing, as he had not opened his mouth or gone through the process of swallowing to equalize the pressure in his ears during the steep dive. In addition, when I pulled the airplane out of the dive and into the zoom, he had seen the struts bend, the rigging wires become slack and heard a cracking sound all over the ship; so he did not think it was a very healthy place, particularly as we had no parachutes.

The other ranking officer who wanted a ride was a red-headed Irishman, a great sportsman and a fine fellow. I repeated the same maneuvers with him, then put the ship into tight spirals, power spins, barrel rolls and a falling leaf, during all of which he kept his head in excellent fashion. It is much harder for a passenger to do this than for a pilot, who knows what is coming and prepares for it. As a last maneuver I pulled the airplane into the top of a loop, let it stall there and then fall on its back for 200 or 300 feet, with our whole weight coming into the belts. Still he seemed to be having just as good a time as I was. In trying the same maneuver again, I shut off my motor a little too quickly and in flying upside down a slight back pressure of air on the propellor stalled the engine. I tried to start it again by a rapid dive, a twist and by maneuvering the spark, but it would not start. We were exactly over St. Elizabeth's Insane Asylum, and it looked as though we might become involuntary inmates of the institution at any moment. Fortunately I succeeded in maneuvering the ship to the edge of the flying field and landed without mishap. The colonel, still unruffled, got out of the ship and told me what a remarkable time he had, and how he enjoyed seeing the motor cut off and the airplane landed with a dead stick. I never told him how nearly he came to being smashed up when the engine stopped.

Shortly after this it became necessary to re-cover one of the wings with fabric. In stripping off the old fabric, we found that the pins on the ends of the wires that brace the inside of the wing had not been fastened with clevis pins where they came through on the other side of the wooden braces, with the result that they had pulled out about halfway. A little more stunting with this plane would have made it collapse entirely.

Another time, in the development of winter flying, I took Captain Christie, the British Air Attaché, with me to Camp Borden, Canada. Lieutenant Bissell, my aide, and Woodruff, a mechanic,

AVIATION

accompanied us in another ship. The temperature was a little above zero as we flew across Lake St. Clair, escorted by about thirty airplanes of the First Pursuit Group. This lake is about twenty miles wide, and it was full of floating ice. The ceiling was not more than 500 feet, and a forced landing under these conditions would have resulted almost surely in the loss of the plane and its occupants.

There was very little snow on the ground when we took off, and we had been informed that there was less than eighteen inches at Camp Borden, so I decided to use wheels instead of skis, as our skis were none too good. When we arrived at the International Boundary the First Pursuit Group turned back and we continued on our way.

Upon checking my compasses on the shore of Lake Huron, I found them to be sixty degrees off for some unaccountable reason. Having found this out, we kept on our true course. Soon we began to notice that the snow was getting deeper; fences along the fields disappeared. As we went farther a few roads could be made out, but the rest were covered with snow. Then we saw a snowplow on a railroad, tossing snow in all directions. After proceeding about 150 miles I decided to go down to a railroad station and read the name, to be sure we were on our course. I came down within thirty or forty feet of a station, read the name and, just as we shot by the back of it, there was an old man with long whiskers driving a team of horses hitched to a bobsleigh. They ran away and threw the old man into a drift of snow, and as we left we could just see his head and whiskers sticking out above it. Then we knew that we would certainly have trouble landing in such deep snow.

When we reached Camp Borden we looked down and saw the members of the Canadian Air Force running around the airdrome on snowshoes. They had made a circle of charcoal on the snow to indicate where we should land. I signaled to Bissell that I would land and that he should stand by and see what happened, then use his own judgment. After telling Christie to remove his goggles and prepare for a turnover, I came down with the slowest speed possible and landed in the deep snow just at the edge of the circle. My airplane went ahead in the snow a little way, to the exact center of the circle, then slowly went up on its nose and stayed there. There was no particular jar or shock. I had not hurt the airplane in any way outside of straining the landing gear a little. I looked back at Christie, and he was clapping his hands to show his approval of the kind of landing we had made.

Landing in Deep Snow at Camp Borden, Canada. The Airplane Was Equipped with Wheels

General Mitchell Taking Off in an Airplane Equipped with Skis

Ezra Meeker, Who Crossed the Continent by Ox Team Sixty Years Ago, Standing Beside Lieutenant Kelly Who, with Lieutenant Macready, Flew from New York City to San Diego, California, in Twenty-Seven Hours

AVIATION

In the meantime Bissell, in the other plane, had been watching me carefully. He decided he could make no better landing than I did, so he told Woodruff to take off his goggles and fold his arms in front of his head as they landed, to protect himself from the shock. He shut off his main gas tank and let the pressure out of it to guard against an explosion, and shifted his engine on to the small emergency gravity tank in the upper wing. He looked to see if any grass was sticking up through the snow, because this, he thought, would be an indication of a rise of ground where the wind had blown the snow away, and at that place there would only be a few inches of snow. Having found the place he thought was suitable he came down, stalled his ship about six feet above the ground and let it fall into the snow. Down it went into the snow for several feet, because what he supposed was grass was the tops of trees sticking out of a ravine that was filled straight across with snow. No one was hurt, but it damaged his undercarriage and propellor, and the Canadians had to shovel out a trail to the place and then bring horses to plow out a space around the airplane before they could extricate it.

When we returned, a few days later, we fitted our airplanes with skis. We found that the snow was so mushy and wet we could not get off easily.

The effect of wet snow is to suck the skis right down into it, and the air cannot get under them. So the evening before we were to leave I had two pieces of log dragged across the snow in the direction of the wind. During the night this trail froze hard and I was able to get off the following morning without any trouble.

From a flying field near Detroit, I once took Mrs. Mitchell with me for a flight across Lake St. Clair, the St. Clair River and over Lake Huron. We were having a beautiful trip, flying at low altitude, seeing the boats in the river and the people going about their daily work in the small towns. As we flew at twenty or thirty feet elevation over the fields, flocks of sheep would run together, the chickens would fly in all directions, the cattle would look at us in wonder or move away slowly, and horses would scamper all about. After flying over the lake a few miles I turned around and began climbing the ship to a high altitude toward some thick clouds, so as to show my wife what flying in clouds and fog was like. We went up through three successive layers of clouds and could no longer see the ground. I was flying by compass for direction and keeping track of where we were by dead reckoning. At about 11,000-feet altitude the engine suddenly gave a couple of splutters and stopped absolutely dead.

AVIATION

We had run out of gas! I estimated that we were over the middle of Lake St. Clair, which is about twenty miles wide, and from that altitude we could glide eight or ten miles. However, it was possible we might have to land in the water, or we might find the clouds so close to the ground when we emerged from them that it would be better to land in water than run the risk of a crash on land.

Gliding for a long distance in an airplane with the motor shut off is very pleasant. There is no noise whatever, very little singing of the wind through the rigging, and the utmost calm prevails, except that in this case there was the disturbing thought that the other end of the glide might end in a bad smash. The ship we were in was so light I could almost land it on a postage stamp. We came through the three layers of clouds again, and as we emerged we were about 4500 feet up, over the south side of Lake St. Clair and within easy gliding distance of Selfridge Field, the Government airdrome, where we landed without mishap.

Another time, in the Hawaiian Islands, I had Mrs. Mitchell with me in the airplane, and accompanying us were two or three other planes. We had flown around the island of Oahu and were looking at the extinct volcanoes, sharp headlands, beautiful water and coral bottoms. We landed and ate luncheon, after which we had some good plover shooting and then started to return. As we took off, tremendous seas were running in and breaking on the beach and on one of the headlands, where the spray was being thrown up several hundred feet in the air from the terrific impact of the breakers. The air was very rough over this place, as we were flying within 200 feet of the ground. This was due not only to the force of the wind blowing against the cliff and being projected upward but also, as the great waves receded, a vacuum was being created on the face of the cliff which had to be filled by air.

The grandeur and majesty of Nature's forces that were unleashed there made us think how puny were the efforts of man in comparison. While enjoying this magnificent spectacle I looked back and saw Lieutenant Eubanks, with another officer in the back seat of his plane, gliding for the water. The propellor was turning over slower and slower, and I saw that the plane was in trouble. If they had had to land in the water with the tremendous seas that were running, we could never have extricated them alive, but as the plane came to within fifteen feet of the water the motor picked up again and we proceeded safely to our destination.

Sometimes we have to land in the water, and there is no difficulty about it if the water is fairly smooth and the pilot keeps his head. Once I had to land in the middle of the Ohio River when my motor stopped as I was climbing out of a deep valley near Moundsville, West Virginia. Below me and a little to one side was the river, and all around were precipitous banks. Not a second was to be lost or the ship would be in a stall, as I was climbing; so I put her head down until I obtained a little more speed, then turned her into the wind and landed with the minimum speed in the river. The airplane rested on an even keel for a few moments, then slowly went up on its nose to an angle of forty-five degrees and stayed there. Neither the mechanic in the back seat nor I in the front was wet. The excitement of the people on shore was so great that they forgot all about coming out to us in a boat. I had to swim ashore and get one. Starting back in it I noticed a man coming at great speed in a canoe to Woodruff's rescue. He was the only one who seemed to have any presence of mind. Later he told us that he had started out from New York and was making a water trip in his frail craft all the way to New Orleans.

The shores of the river here contained a great number of old apple trees. The tradition is that a man called Apple Tree Johnny had gone down the Ohio River before the coming of the settlers and

SKYWAYS

planted fruit trees and vegetables so they could have them when they came. On the opposite side of the river, just back of the town of Moundsville, are the great mounds constructed by the prehistoric mound builders, which are in plain view from the air.

When we first began to use airplanes we used to shoot ducks out of them sometimes. We even tied a couple of automatic shot guns on the struts and fired them by pulling a string attached to the triggers. We would start up a flock of ducks by flying close to the water, then keep close behind them and fire the guns, killing a great number. An observer on the ground watched where they fell and picked them up. It was not a very sporting practice, so we soon stopped it. We also found we could shoot deer from airplanes with machine guns, but this was soon stopped for the same reason.

If a shotgun is fired directly ahead of an airplane, within a few seconds the plane will run right into the shot. This is because the shot has an initial velocity of 900 feet a minute, which falls off very rapidly, until at sixty yards it has only about 400-feet velocity left, and at 100 yards it has none. An airplane going 100 miles an hour covers 100 yards in two seconds, which does not give the shot time to drop.

AVIATION

One of my airplanes was arranged so that I could put two dogs in it for bird shooting. In this way I was able to go wherever the shooting was good, enjoy several hours' sport, then return in a very short time. The dogs became accustomed to riding in airplanes just as they do in automobiles, and would lie still and behave themselves in splendid fashion.

Once Lieutenant Bissell, one of my aides, brought a dog to me across the Alleghany Mountains, together with a couple of sacks full of Chesapeake Bay oysters. The vibration of the plane made the sharp edges of the oysters cut through the sacks, then cut through the fabric of the fuselage and fall out, with the result that he left a trail of oysters through the middle of the Alleghany Mountains. People must have wondered greatly when they found fresh oysters along a lonely mountain trail and dripping from the trees and bushes.

We used to carry canvasback ducks and fish caught in the morning in Chesapeake Bay, and dine that evening on them in Detroit, Milwaukee or Chicago. I had another airplane especially fixed up for duck hunting, which is usually better during heavy storms, rain and snow. This ship had an arrangement for the pilot and mechanic to sit side by side instead of one behind the other. We made many trips through storms and learned a great deal about them. One time we landed just about sunrise on the banks of the Wicomico River, sixty miles from Washington, got into our blinds, killed our limit of canvasbacks in four hours, and started to return. The storm had become so intense and the ground was covered so deeply with snow that all traffic was held up. We took off in the face of it, although I could hardly see half a mile ahead of me. In spite of the ship being somewhat covered with ice, we made good time. As we flew up the Potomac we could see that all railway traffic was held up, as well as automobiles on the roads. Boats could not navigate the Potomac River. Domestic animals were all huddled up in their stables. When we landed at Bolling Field, the noise of the wind and storm was so great that the crew on duty did not even hear us alight. The airplane was the only means of transportation that could go straight through such conditions.

Many years ago in El Paso, Texas, Captain—now Colonel—Hanney of the Infantry and I started into the Sacramento Mountains to kill some deer. We reached our destination and within a few hours I had killed two black-tailed deer. Captain Hanney had killed one, and as he was looking for the second his orderly called suddenly, "Captain—

Captain, look at the tiger!" Looking about, he saw a large jaguar disappear over the crest of a hill. We followed him to his den in the face of a vertical cliff about 2000 feet high. With our equipment it was impossible for us to get down to the den, which was some 200 feet down a sheer precipice; so we decided to return to El Paso and fix up some ropes for getting down there, also some smoke balls to throw into the den, consisting of woolen yarn dipped in turpentine, then rolled in red pepper and gunpowder. When set on fire, these balls made a thick suffocating smoke mixed with red pepper that would drive the animals out. I was interrupted in my preparations by being ordered to Washington on the General Staff. Some years afterward, at the conclusion of the European war, I flew into El Paso in my plane. I thought of the time we had hunted the jaguar, so I flew into the mountains and found the canyon where the jaguars lived, saw the den and, from the indications around it, I am sure the jaguars were still there at that time, and probably are today.

From our planes we often look for fish, porpoises, sharks and giant rays, or devil-fish. In certain stages of the sun and in clear water they are very easy to see.

Flying in different parts of the world, taking up

people of different nationalities and seeing their reaction has a great fascination. When the Prince of Wales was staying with me on the Rhine, just after the Armistice, I took him on quite a long trip up the Moselle River, then across to the Rhine and around the area occupied by the American Army. All the old castles were spread out before us, of which the Prince knew all the legends, the owners and former occupants. We crossed the Rhine at the Lorelei and saw the Drachenfels with its ruined castle on top. Although it was during the first part of January, the sun came out fitfully through the clouds, affording us a remarkable display of lights and shadows on the ground. Over Neuweid, at an altitude of 4000 feet, we saw the princess of Neuweid in her garden, with a large white bulldog which she always kept with her. As we approached the landing field again, we could see the old Roman edifices along the bank of the Moselle that were erected in Cæsar's time.

At another time, in the Philippines, I took up General Aguinaldo, the leader of the Philippine insurrection in 1899. We flew over the places where we had fought in the campaign twenty-five years before, then along the west coast of the island of Luzon over Mariveles Mountain, an extinct volcano, then over to Cavite Province, where Agui-

General Mitchell Taking General Aguinaldo, Formerly Head of the Philippine Insurrection, for a Trip in the Air

Manila, P. I., from the Air, Showing the Great Detail in Which Objects on the Ground are Represented

KING LUCAS OF THE NEGRITOS AND SOME OF HIS TRIBE

GENERAL AND MRS. MITCHELL WITH KING LUCAS AND HIS QUEEN

naldo was born. We could see Taal volcano, which is in the middle of a lake and erupts mud. This mud has caustic properties which cause it to burn up vegetation and make sores on cattle and livestock. Volcanoes may erupt mud, like Taal, or ashes, like the Mayon volcano, also in the Philippines, or lava, like Vesuvius. As we passed over the various towns, General Aguinaldo, who of course could read the map as well as any of us, recognized everything; and to show the people on the ground that he had flown over, he frequently dropped his calling card, hoping that somebody would find it. I have never seen a person more keenly observant on his first air trip, or one who enjoyed it more.

A few days after this, Mrs. Mitchell and I went into the northern part of the island of Luzon, among the savages and head hunters. At Camp Stotsenburg, General Hagood had invited the tribes of Negritos to come in and see us and have a feast on some old horses that were to be killed for that purpose. These people are among the most primitive in existence. They are diminutive in stature, only about four feet high. Their characteristics are distinctly Negroid—black skin, thick lips, flat noses and very curly bushy hair. They do not know how to make fires, and eat only roots and raw meat. They file their front teeth sharp, so as to be able to tear the raw meat more easily. They live in little wickiups around the roots of trees, in hollow trees and even up in the branches.

Their king, Lucas by name, brought with him one of his wives and a small baby that weighed about two pounds. General Hagood had had a uniform made for Lucas and presented him with a sword, while we decorated him with a medal, made of the top of a tomato can, and called "The Order of the Dead Horse." Then I took him up in the air. We tied him in securely, and the poor little creature put his head down in the cockpit and remained perfectly quiet. Only once did he see the ground—when I tilted the airplane up sideways and slipped it so he could look out without putting his head up. I landed after a few minutes, and all his people trooped up around him to hear what he had to say. Immediately the airplane was on the ground, all fear left him and he stood up in the cockpit and told them all about the flight. He reminded me very much of some of his white brothers who never see anything in the air, but when they get down tell all about it.

A short time after this we went up to visit Marshal Chang Tso-Lin, the war lord of Manchuria, at Mukden. I had known him a great many years

AVIATION

and he was always an interesting character to me. He had some new French airplanes that were very good and well kept up; also he was building some large new arsenals to manufacture guns and ammunition. I thought, while I was flying one of his new ships, that I might just as well take some photographs of what was going on. So I told my aide to take my camera and photograph all the new military works in that vicinity. I asked him if he knew how to work the camera, and he said he did. After flying around for an hour or so, and using up a couple of rolls of film, we landed. To my great disappointment, I found that he had just been pressing the release on the shutter, instead of setting it and then pressing it; consequently the photographs were all blanks. I told General Chang about it, as I thought it was too good a joke to keep. He laughed heartily and told me it was in return for a joke I told him many years before, when he invited me to dinner. The flies were very bad and lit on his bald head; so he asked me how I thought he could get rid of them. I advised him to tattoo a spider's web on his head and then the flies would be scared and stay away! He had never forgotten this.

In Siam, Java, India and other parts of Asia the air gives more of a picture of conditions than does any other means of travel. The wastes of the north, the deserts and the dense forests form a never-ending source of interest to the flyer. As the world has become so well known both on the ground and the water, there remains little for the venting of the spirit of sport and adventure except the air.

The flying of gliders is an interesting and delightful pastime. The ordinary glider is built similarly to an airplane, but without an engine; consequently it is very lightly loaded and has comparatively large surfaces. Thus, every advantage can be taken of up-currents of air for sustaining or carrying the glider to greater altitudes. The power imparted by the air to the glider is the same as that which sustains vultures and other birds of that type in their gliding and soaring flight.

The delight of motorless flying lies in its quietness, the absence of vibration, the delicacy of touch required to handle the controls, the slowness with which one is able to land, and the remarkable property which the glider has of going up and down in the air due to ascending and descending currents. It gives one a knowledge of movements in the air to an even greater extent than is obtained in free ballooning. Free ballooning has been a sport for more than 150 years, but since the coming of the airplane it has diminished somewhat in importance and popularity.

Anyone who can fly an airplane even passably is able to handle a glider. They are given their initial velocity, or starting speed, by being pulled along the ground downhill, or by spring arrangements, something like a catapult. We used to take a lot of shock-absorber cord, to a length of about 100 feet, hook it to the glider, pulling it out to its maximum of elasticity, then let it pull the glider forward until it took the air. The hook would disengage itself when the cord became slack. Gliders may also take off from cliffs, high buildings or from airplanes and airships.

Gliders also may be towed behind airplanes or airships in much the same way that an aquaplane is towed behind a motor boat. The glider may be kept in constant telephonic communication with the airplane or airship through the cable which tows it. A drum with spring mechanism in it to take up the shock of slackening or tightening the cable may be installed in the airplane in much the same way that a towing machine is placed in a tug on the water. A towed glider, especially behind an airplane flying at great speed, will give the operator sensations and thrills that can be obtained in no other way.

S K Y W A Y S

Aviation for sport is organized along quite solid and practical lines in England in light-airplane clubs. They receive certain assistance from the government, and their members obtain free instruction in flying, besides other privileges. They stage competitions and flying meets, and do much toward popularizing and advancing aviation. In the United States, airplane country clubs are beginning to be organized under the auspices of certain organizations interested in the production and sale of airplanes.

CHAPTER XV

A MODERN AIR LINER

THE best way to get an idea of what air traffic is and what it holds for the future is to make a flight in a modern passenger air liner along one of the world's great airways. In Europe, regular commercial lines are established between all great centers of population and are almost as well known and regularly patronized as other forms of travel on land or sea. The following is an account of a flight that I made in a German commercial airplane from Berlin, Germany, to Moscow, Russia, in twelve hours.

To go to Russia in former times required a journey of many days. During recent years, it has been almost impossible to go there with any degree of safety and comfort. Now that some order is coming out of chaos, not only are the railways running on schedule time throughout Russia, but airways have been established from Germany to the center of the Soviet Republic. Great passenger aircraft maintain schedules as punctual as those of trains or steamships and make the trip in about one fourth or one sixth the time required by other means of transportation.

The plane for Moscow leaves Berlin at 2 o'clock in the morning. Motor busses leave the center of the city at 1:30 A.M. for Templehofer Field. There one's luggage is weighed and inspected, thirty-five pounds being allowed to each traveler, and each piece is marked with the owner's name and where he is going. Passports are exhibited and the airplane is cleared for its destination. The planes used are fine 3-engine all metal ships, equipped with comfortable, upholstered armchairs.

We found our airplane waiting at the edge of a concrete runway. It was pitch dark overhead of course, but lights illuminated everything necessary on the airport. We entered and took our seats, and the signal was given to start the engines, which all began at once. Long exhaust pipes carried the explosions from the engines well out to the trailing edge of the wings, where they showed with a pale blue light in the darkness of the night.

Precisely on the minute the signal was given to leave, and without further ado, the airplane rose into the air. A bow light, port and starboard lights and a stern light were carried, just as on a vessel at sea. The lights of the sleeping city showed brightly below, and as the silent town was crossed, the first air beacon, in the shape of a rotating searchlight, was seen away ahead along the airway.

A MODERN AIR LINER

Every twenty miles there is one of these beacons, and between them, every four or five miles, are bright red lights placed on the ground, which indicate where an emergency landing may be made.

Every five minutes weather reports came in to the radio operator, who sat at his instruments in the forward part of the plane's cabin. He could communicate with the ground either by telephone or telegraph, and was notified immediately by the weather service of any storm or fog ahead, and what should be done under the circumstances. The pilot was a man who had flown before the war, all through the war and ever since the war. Beside him sat a mechanic of many years' experience, who was also capable of flying the plane and landing it, in case anything happened to the pilot. He watched the instruments on the engines and on the instrument board, which were all illuminated, to see that everything was working properly. In the middle of the pilot's instruments was a large gyroscopic indicator, which would tell the airplane's attitude on the darkest night or in a fog.

The passengers looked out of the windows at the cities passing beneath them, brightly lighted by street lamps, and at the rivers and forests, which could be distinguished vaguely. The engines purred along and one after another the passengers dropped off to sleep.

Two hours passed and something awakened everyone. The engines had ceased to turn up to their cruising rate and the airplane was gliding. Everyone looked out and saw a beacon directly underneath, revolving around an arc which covered several miles in the sky. Red lights marked the corners of the landing field, and a couple of flood lights disclosed the presence of some hangars. Dantzig, on the Baltic Sea, was below us. While the pilot maneuvered for a landing, bright flares with flying sparks were ignited under each of the plane's wings and the ground below was illuminated almost as plainly as in the daytime. The airplane landed without a jar and taxied up to the waiting hangars. The passengers got out and went to a warm rest room in the airport, while the mail and express was taken out and the whole airplane was thoroughly inspected.

Soon the signal was given to leave, the passengers resumed their places and the airplane took off in the dark. The airdrome was not lighted, merely guide lights showing on the ground. The plane rose smoothly and the lights of Dantzig disappeared. In the breaking light of the new day, the airplane threaded its way across the Baltic Sea.

A MODERN AIR LINER

One hour from Dantzig, Koenigsberg, the metropolis of East Prussia, was reached. In the old days this was a powerful military stronghold of the Germans on the Russian frontier. Now the country opposite is the Republic of Lithuania, and the military atmosphere that formerly pervaded it has disappeared. One detects a Russian influence in the appearance of the people, the construction of the houses and the manner in which the food is prepared. An excellent breakfast of ham and eggs, coffee and rolls was furnished. The coffee was beginning to be poor, because in this part of the world everybody drinks tea.

The passengers now changed to a single engine plane, smaller but just as comfortable, with places for six passengers instead of ten. There was no radio operator aboard, only a pilot and mechanic. The ship was an underslung monoplane, that is, the body of the airplane was under the wing, so an unobstructed view of the country could be obtained.

Gradually the neat towns, brick and stone houses, well paved roads and splendidly cultivated fields of East Prussia gave way to log houses, thatched roofs, unpaved roads. Flocks and herds of goats, cattle, sheep and pigs were everywhere. We noticed that the towns were built around churches, gleaming white in the morning sun, with onion-shaped domes surmounting their towers covered with bright gold, and crowned with the cross of the Greek church.

We flew over Kovno, the junction point of the two branches of the Dwina River. Lake after lake passed us in unbroken sequence. We had entered the great marsh area which bounds Russia on the west. Minsk was only a little way south of our route. Pinsk and the Pripet swamps are a tremendous barrier which always protected Russia from Europe, and which in turn protected Europe from the ancient invasion of Huns and Tartars.

The floods this year had been very bad. There is no drainage, the water merely lies on the flat ground. The poor peasants' grain had been spoiled and many of their animals foundered or drowned. Everywhere possible they had taken their wheat to high ground and spread it out so it would dry, but in many cases even the elevations, which are only a few feet above the surrounding territory, had been covered by the flood waters. Transportation on the ground was difficult, in places well nigh impossible. The roads were worse than those we used to have in Virginia before the gasoline tax gave the State government something to build roads with. There were no motor vehicles anywhere. We saw horses and wagons carrying the big bow at the end of the shafts over the horse's neck, which is characteristic of Russia. The houses were of logs with thatched roofs, most of them arranged in the form of a quadrangle, with the living quarters on one side, stable and cattle sheds on another and store houses completing the square. In the evening the cattle are driven into the enclosures for protection and safety. From the air one can see and fully appreciate the primitive conditions under which people live. It was a wild country, full of dense forests and lonely marshes. I remembered some tales I had heard of its being overrun with wolves who sometimes attacked human beings.

One, two, three hours passed after Koenigsberg, and we were deep into Russia. The country continued the same, monotonous, flat and uninteresting plains, much like flying over Ohio, Illinois and Kansas in our own country, as far as scenery was concerned.

One of my fellow passengers was a German from the great steel center, Essen. He was as well equipped with maps, guide books and "dope" of all kinds on Russia as myself. An old balloonist, he formerly competed in the James Gordon Bennett Balloon races, and was a great enthusiast about air transportation. It was his first trip into Russia and he observed every place with the greatest interest, in fact he did not miss a trick on the way in. It amused me to see what a good eye he had for things on the ground seen from an airplane, which only comes from much experience in flying. The average person who flies for the first few times is entirely incapable of telling what he sees on the ground.

He and I became fast friends by the end of the journey. He spoke English just about as well or badly as I spoke German, so we compromised by speaking French. He had been to America and was a great believer in American institutions. I found him to be a highly educated and gifted man, and a strong Democrat, being decidedly against the former German government and the Kaiser, and attributing most of Germany's ills to the former militaristic attitude of the old Empire.

Five hours out from Koenigsberg, we saw a large city. The mechanic came back into the passenger compartment announcing that the orders of the military commander of Smolensk were that the curtains must be pulled down so the passengers would not see the surroundings of the town. This place is one of the main garrisons of the Russian Army which guard the approaches to Moscow, and is full of soldiers, fortifications and military works.

A MODERN AIR LINER

We saw it all by peeping out of the curtained windows.

We landed for the first time in Russia on the military airdrome at Smolensk, at one side of which were hangars for the Russian military air forces. Twenty or thirty airplanes were lined up in front of them. The Russians are working hard on their air force and doing everything possible to make it so formidable that outside nations may be held off in case of attack. Although the general organization of the air field was modeled after German lines, it appeared slovenly and unkempt. The personnel on the airdrome were not so well instructed or alert as the Germans, and spoke nothing but Russian and a few words of German. The edifices and houses were of wooden construction and quite simple.

The people passing by looked poor, illiterate and extremely suspicious. We felt that we were in a different world, or another age, just as though Time had been put back two or three hundred years. Peasant women walked along the roads in bare feet, carrying heavy packs on their backs, and horses drew primitive wagons along the rough highways. The men wore long shirts on the outside of their trousers, with a belt around the waist, a small cap with a peak, and high boots. Boots are necessary on account of the mud all over the country. A few soldiers, fine big physical specimens, rather cleaner than the ordinary run of the people, strolled over to the airplane and looked at it. Everybody else was kept away from the airdrome by strong barbed wire fences and by guards.

After the airplane was thoroughly inspected and refueled, and everyone had had something to eat, we took to the air again. The country was still flat but was gradually becoming a little dryer. Little villages were grouped around highways, and outlying farms stretched into the woods. We had passed the area of swamps that reaches for five or six hundred miles across Europe from the Baltic Sea to the Carpathian Mountains.

An hour and a quarter's flight brought us to the battlefield of Borodino, which is well marked by monuments and a great monastery in the center, erected after the battle. Here in 1812 Napoleon crushed the Russian force, but at a terrible cost to himself, because the Russian resistance was so tenacious that he had to launch his Old Guard into the center of their positions. These wonderful troops were badly used up, which led indirectly to his ruin in the end. How any thinking person one hundred years ago could attempt to rush into Moscow across this trackless country covered by swamps, with no resources, and above all, in the fall of the year when they were sure to be caught by the frosts and snow, passes all imagination. It is what caused the downfall of Napoleon. Led on by thoughts of world dominion and a desire to emulate the deeds of Alexander the Great, he broke his force against the natural features of the Russian vastnesses. At that time it took him six weeks to go in or come out. With our airplanes we had covered the distance to Borodino in eleven hours from Berlin. The air has no frontier and wherever there is air, airplanes can go. Russia today lies open to air attack. Its swamps are no longer a great protection.

By two o'clock, the increasing number of villages indicated our approach to Moscow. The great city burst into view as a gleam of the sun through the clouds shone on the tremendous golden domes of the cathedral of Saint Sauveur. We were above the old Muscovite capital, an Oriental rather than a European city, the seat of the Soviet government and the least known and least understood great capital in the world today.

After a turn over the military airdrome, a beautiful big grassy field close to the city, our pilot brought the airplane to rest. Many planes were rising and landing, and as we taxied to the hangars of the commercial ships, I noticed DH airplanes with American Liberty engines being used by the Russian aviation school to give instruction to pilots. Airplanes of many types were all over the place, pursuit single seaters both monoplanes and biplanes, two seaters, observation ships and others.

As we stepped out of the ship, our baggage was taken to the customhouse. A company of soldiers passed by us, great tall men in high boots with their long shirts belted at the waist. Their step was slow, almost majestic, not over eighty-five to the minute. As they went along, one of their non-commissioned officers began to sing, then the whole column took up the chorus and filled the air with their great sonorous voices as they strode along.

Beside the airdrome is a large church with many domes, to which Napoleon moved from Moscow when the city was given over to flames, which lasted for four days.

Our baggage was inspected with the utmost care. Every piece of paper that was contained in it was carefully scrutinized, except my own, which was passed without comment. Only my camera, which I had been informed I could take in without trouble, was seized. Russians are very careful about not allowing anyone to take photographs which might be used as propaganda against them. I could easily have concealed the camera had I wished to, but their officials had been so open handed and straightforward about letting me come in that I told them exactly what I had and what I wanted to do with it.

We were now in Russia and the trip in had been one of the most interesting, comfortable and pleasant that I had ever taken. The whole thing had been arranged by the German Luft Hansa. Mr. Merkle, the president, had brought me into contact with the Russian Air Ministry and had done everything possible to further my desire of seeing Russia and Russian aviation. Up to the border at Koenigsberg, where we changed from a 3-engine to a single engine airplane, the planes were German owned, operated by the Luft Hansa; but from Koenigsberg to Moscow, a company called the Deruluft, half German and half Russian, is the operating organization. This is fortunate for the Russians because in organizing and handling airways and flying over them, the Germans are most expert.

We were given passes to leave the airdrome, which we handed to a sentinel who guarded the gateway. He was a great big six-footer, looking about as intelligent as a Newfoundland puppy. I am sure he could not read, and so could not tell what was on our passes but he saw the official stamp and knew it was all right. Although he looked dirty and his uniform was more or less unkempt, his rifle with bayonet attached was beautifully clean, and the cartridges and ammunition looked in excellent shape.

Outside a big Benz touring car awaited us, in which we proceeded to Moscow.

Air transportation is an accomplished fact in Europe, as distinguished from America where there are no real through passenger airlines. Each great city has its airport which is arranged similar to a seaport. It has a station with every comfort for the traveler, waiting rooms, restaurants, news stands, baggage checkrooms, customs houses for the inspection of passengers, medical and sanitary control and police protection.

Aircraft come and go on regular schedule. The airways are maintained like automobile highways across country. Every few miles there are places where planes may land in case of trouble and obtain mechanical assistance, spare parts, fuel and oil.

The radio telegraphic service is highly perfected. Besides transmitting ordinary messages and weather reports, there is a radio compass system which keeps in touch with each airplane as it moves across country, so that its location is known at all times. The weather system is especially good. Observations are made each hour along the route which an airplane is following. The weather reports are

Commercial Airplane of the German Luft-Hansa at Templehofer Airdrome Near Berlin, Germany

THE GREAT FRENCH AIRPORT OF LE BOURGET, FRANCE

A MODERN AIR LINER

sent by radio to all airports a minute or two after they are made and are immediately posted upon a large wall map of the airways. As the pilots who fly the air liners speak many different languages, English, French, Dutch, Italian and German, weather conditions are indicated on the maps by conventional signs instead of by words. The weather is shown not only as of the last observation, but also of an hour before, so that the pilot himself may be able to judge of the change that has occurred.

The pilots have to register on a recording instrument, like a time clock, when they leave the weather report room. The airplane is then cleared by the airport authorities and constant radio communication is maintained with it while in flight until it reaches its destination.

All pilots and airplanes are carefully inspected and kept under constant observation as to their physical condition and airworthiness.

When I visited the French airport at Le Bourget, just outside Paris, a very heavy rain was falling, with fitful winds and low clouds to the westward. Notwithstanding these conditions, the great air liners scheduled to go to London and other European airports were ready, the largest of which

SKYWAYS were the French and British planes on the Paris-London service.

The French liner belonging to the United French Airlines had nine hundred horsepower, in two 450 horsepower engines, one of which could practically hold the plane in flight if the other stopped. The plane itself had every safety device to prevent fires and guard against motor stoppages, together with all the navigation aids possible to install. It was equipped with radio, both telephone and telegraph. It had an exceptionally strong landing gear and landed very slowly, which is one of the greatest guaranties of safety. Seats were arranged for eighteen passengers, with tables between them which could be used for reading, writing, playing games; or meals could be served on them during the trip. There was a fully equipped kitchen in the nose of the plane, with electric stoves and other conveniences. A cook and a waiter prepared and distributed the meals while in transit, just as on a dining car on our own railroads.

The other large liner making ready to take off was a three-engine, 20-passenger Handley Page airplane, of the British Imperial Airway System. It had thirteen hundred and fifty horsepower, and was able to fly on two of its three 450 h. p. engines

A MODERN AIR LINER

if one failed. Every convenience and luxury for air travel and every possible safety device was provided.

While we watched, eighteen passengers boarded the liner, handing their small hand luggage to the attendant who stored it in the baggage compartment. They were shown to their seats as in a railway carriage, sat down and began reading papers or magazines, or chatted with one another just as they would on a steamship or other carrier. Just as it left, a Dutch air liner from Amsterdam came in, carrying eight passengers, arriving on schedule time right through the storm and clouds. Other airplanes were preparing to leave for Marseilles on the Mediterranean, where connection is made with lines running to Africa; others for Strasbourg in Alsace, where one makes connections for Austria and Turkey, and for Germany and Russia.

One outstanding feature of European air travel is that it has definitely proved that passenger air traffic can be carried on safely, comfortably and on schedule time. Naturally the whole matter is still in its development stage, with a tremendous future ahead of it.

The lesson for America to learn is that with intelligent government supervision, which is absolutely

SKYWAYS

necessary in the present development of aeronautics, the United States, with the natural ability of our people, our splendid factories and our boundless raw materials for constructing aircraft, can easily be the leading air power of the world.

CHAPTER XVI

A GLANCE AT WORLD AERONAUTICS

As EACH nation of the world has its own particular problems, it organizes, administers and employs its aviation to meet these needs. The basis of all their organizations is military, because that is the predominant value of aviation to the state. It is their offensive arm *par excellence*. Aviation must attack to bring about results. It cannot dig trenches or dugouts in the air and assume the defensive. It must go after its adversary, wherever he is, and either destroy him or be destroyed. There is no middle course.

England, whose far-flung empire extends to all parts of the world, is herself confined to a comparatively small, thickly populated insular territory just off the coast of a continent. The English Channel is only eighteen miles wide. With modern airplanes, from points in France, Belgium, Holland or Germany, London and other great cities of England can be reached in an hour and a half. Even from Russia, Austria, Italy or Spain aircraft may come and throw down their messengers of death and destruction. An army or navy is powerless to prevent an incursion of this kind. The only thing that can fight it is an air force.

England, therefore, has an air force acting under a Minister of Aviation, and coequal in importance with the army and navy. It is intrusted with the defense of the British Isles and the seas up to within 200 miles of the islands. This leaves the navy free to get out in the ocean away from the coast and carry out its mission of keeping water areas clear for British commerce. What little aviation the army and navy need for their own domestic use is assigned them from the Royal Air Force, but the main part of Great Britain's air strength is concentrated into one command under its own chiefs and its own ministry.

The Air Ministry is organized into three principal departments—military, civil, and engineering and research. The military department has to do with all military functions of aircraft. The department of civil aviation encourages commercial air traffic, sees that suitable and safe airplanes are employed, that the pilots operating them are instructed in their duties and capable of handling transport airplanes. It regulates and pays a subsidy to civilian aircraft. It provides for airports, landing fields, airways, all the aids to air navigation, a meteorological service, the dissemination of information about aeronautics, and looks after the organization of propaganda societies and civilian clubs which will back up the Ministry of Aviation in a political way. The department of experimentation and engineering studies new types of aircraft, together with all safety devices, instruments, armament and auxiliaries.

In case of war every element of the British air power is instantly handled from one headquarters. It is both simple and effective. The British aeronautical organization can well be used as a model for any country to follow. In each of the dominions and in India a department of aviation is maintained, modeled on that of the British, but modified to suit local conditions.

The mandated territory of Iraq in the valley of the Tigris and Euphrates rivers has been turned over to the Air Force for administration, instead of to an army commander. The result has been a great economy in its upkeep and maintenance. When the Air Force first occupied the territory some uprisings occurred. The Air Force commander notified the belligerent chiefs that their depredations would have to cease, but they paid no attention to these messages. So a few flights of British airplanes went over and attacked their towns, means of transportation, flocks and herds, and under cover of these attacks, troops were brought up by airplane and the localities occupied. These large transport planes—troopers, as they are called—are equipped to carry twenty soldiers with rifles, machine guns and equipment. The natives know they have no means of resisting air control and consequently peace, law and order prevails. A military occupation by troops alone could never entirely put down all the uprisings of roving bands, which the air force can deal with easily.

The British Air Force has been of incalculable benefit to them in India, where the frontiers have been efficiently patrolled by aircraft. It has held in check uprisings and incursions on the borders of Afghanistan, particularly by the Afridis and Waziri, and by tribes on the borders of Baluchistan. If any armed resistance to British authority occurs in India itself, the Air Force, unaided, is able to cope with it. Great Britain is building dirigible airships and large airplanes to patrol her lines of commerce, because she knows that if these are broken down the inhabitants of the British Isles will starve and her great empire will fall to pieces.

The great air powers of the world all have a similar system of supply. First, there are the airplanes in the hands of the troops. These are of the oldest serviceable types, which are being used up. Next, there are a little better and more efficient airplanes, which are stored in the magazines, ready to issue to the air troops in case of war. Third are airplanes which have been tested by the technical and experimental departments, which are ready to be turned over to the manufacturers for rapid production, and fourth are the airplanes of a type still superior, which are in course of design on the drawing boards of the engineers, almost ready to be built. The airplane factories, motor factories and all those able to fabricate aeronautical equipment are carefully organized and listed, and know exactly what they have to do in case of war.

France, being confronted with warlike neighbors all around and menaced with a constantly decreasing population, has put a great deal of effort and thought into her air force. She has a department of aviation with a minister at its head which is co-equal in importance with the army and navy. France maintains under arms the largest air force now in existence, consisting of about 2000 airplanes. They are able to strike at the capitals and centers of population of any of her neighbors within twenty-four hours' notice. Behind these stand 2000 more airplanes already constructed, ready to be manned by reserves; and behind these a system of supply which will keep these 4000 airplanes equipped with spare planes, parts, engines, armament, fuel and ammunition in case of a severe campaign.

France's allies, Czecho-Slovakia, Poland and Belgium, all have enormous air forces in proportion to the extent and population of their countries. They have been instructed, supplied and equipped with French planes and under the French system. With these allies, France is able to put into the air a greater air force than all the rest of the world combined. This is seldom appreciated by military students when they consider armies and navies solely, and the auxiliary air forces which are attached to them. The French know full well that air power will decide future wars.

In addition to the air force in France, the French maintain an air force in their possession of Morocco, which one of my old comrades, General Armengaud, is now commanding. The air force itself is able to cope with any uprisings of the natives there in the same way that the British do in Iraq. For a long time, when the great insurrection of Abd-el Krim occurred, the French Army attempted to put it down by sending out mobile columns and detachments of ground troops and keeping small garrisons at different places to support these. The Moroccans would wait for a favorable opportunity, then pounce upon these garrisons and destroy them, and be gone as quickly as they came. The French Army merely used the air force as a means of communication between these posts and to supply them with food and ammunition. They were so unsuccessful that they had to listen to the advice of the air commander, who told them that by destroying the pack animals of the Riffs—their camels, horses and means of transportation—and their cattle and goats, on which they subsisted, and menacing their towns from the air, they could be quickly brought to time. When this was done the campaign was rapidly brought to a close and Abd-el Krim surrendered and was sent into exile on the island of Madagascar, with only eight of his twenty-four wives.

The French also maintain a small air service for local use in their possession of Indo-China in Asia. This serves to map the country, carry medical assistance from place to place and keep in touch with the outlying districts where transportation is difficult.

Italy has an excellent air force under a Ministry of Aviation. At the end of the war, the air service, then under the army and navy, was neglected and went all to pieces. The airplanes disintegrated in tumble-down hangars. When Mussolini took charge of the government he organized a single department of national defense, with subsecretaries for the army, navy and air force. This is an ideal organization, as it concentrates command but distributes responsibility to each of the services. The Italian military problem consists in defending themselves against their neighbors and in their hope for control of the Mediterranean Sea in case of hostilities. To the north and east they are bounded by high mountains; consequently their aircraft are designed to climb rapidly and fly at high altitudes. It will be remembered that in the days of the Romans their armies occupied Switzerland. When this was accomplished they could come down from this lofty citadel on to the fertile plains of Gaul, Germany and what is now Austria. It is in the realm of possibility that a great air power occupying Switzerland in the future could from this position of vantage sweep the countries all around it with its cruisers of the airs, because altitude gives a great advantage to aircraft. The Italian factories in the north of Italy turn out as good airplanes as any in the world. They are also very expert in the design and construction of lighter-than-air craft, particularly the semirigid airship, which has some characteristics superior to the rigid airship. They can be made lighter, and consequently carry a greater useful load and rise to higher altitudes.

 The Italian civil aviation is not well developed,

An Italian Caproni Airplane Being Set Up in the Factory at Milan

The Newest Travel Service Single-Seater Pursuit Airplane, the Bernard 20 C1

Swedish Three-Seater All Purpose Military Airplane of Metal Construction Designed and Made by the German Junkers Company in Sweden

as their country is not particularly large and it is expensive to maintain. There is great spirit in the Italian Air Force, handled by able young officers with the spirit of "do" in them—an all-important thing in an air force. The Air Ministry is organized into the usual departments of military and civil aviation, and an experimental department which has in contemplation some of the most interesting developments of any of the powers in aviation.

Spain also has a Ministry of Aviation and is attempting to make this her principal arm of the military service. Her young men are just as good in the air as they are good navigators on the sea. Spain also uses this air force in her African possession of Morocco.

Germany was prohibited by the Treaty of Versailles from having any military aviation. She was the first of the great nations to organize a separate department of aviation, which occurred in 1916, and it was one of the reasons why, with fewer airplanes and pilots than the Allies, she rendered such a wonderful account of herself in the air on every front.

Since the war a company known as the Lufthansa, or aeronautical trust, has been organized, which is practically a department of aviation. Stock has been taken in this company by the Reich, or federal government, by the various states, municipalities, banking institutions and large commercial enterprises, with the result that it has plenty of money. Subsidies are paid by the federal government, cities and municipalities for the airplanes, pilots and passengers carried. Their airways are exceptionally well organized, as are their airports and landing fields. I believe they are the best in existence at the present time. German aircraft are designed to fly at low altitudes, carry heavy weights and be very reliable. Metal construction predominates. Although they lost out for a while after the Armistice in the development of their motors, as this feature was stopped by the Versailles Treaty, they now have excellent engines. Recently Doctor Junkers perfected a Diesel engine for aircraft use which is splendid. A great many types of airplanes are being developed for all sorts of uses and with various speeds, all of them suitable for use in the military service. In case of war, with her great dye factories and chemical industry, Germany could almost overnight load up her great commercial air fleet with toxic gases and cause the complete evacuation of cities such as Paris or London.

The Germans have the greatest passenger-carrying planes in existence. The large Dornier flying boat has carried 169 people. It is equipped with twelve engines, of 525 horse power each, giving

The Dornier DO-X, the World's Largest Airplane

Mr. Dornier, Dr. Eckener, and General Mitchell Standing in Front of a Dornier Airplane

6300 horse power. Doctor Junkers has an extremely interesting new airplane in which the engines are carried inside the wings and the power transmitted by long shafts to the propellors. Diesel aviation engines will probably be installed in this ship at an early date.

German air lines extend to all neighboring states and into Russia. They are assisting the Russians very greatly in the development of their air power, furnishing them with technical assistance and supervision of their factories. German aeronautical engineers have factories in Italy, Sweden and Denmark. They have passenger air service in the summertime that competes to such an extent with the railways as to cut down their income considerably.

Germans are inventive, excellent technicians and thoroughly understand the problems of aviation. Their airship development, with the Zeppelin Foundation at its head, has accomplished wonders. Beginning shortly after the Civil War in our country, Count Zeppelin attacked the problem of dirigible airships. After years of painstaking work he produced one that flew. Accidents and the tremendous expenditures required for experimentation used up all his fortune, but at this point he appealed to the German people to help him, and they generously responded with funds which were put into what amounts to a trust, administered by a committee. No stock is owned and only the cost of experimental work and salaries are paid out of it. The Zeppelin Foundation owns various subsidiary companies, which make duralumin, engines, cloth, even airplanes, motor cars and railroad carriages. The profits from all these things go back into the central fund. Doctor Eckener, an associate of Count Zeppelin for many years, who recently commanded the airship Graf Zeppelin on its trip around the world, is the active head of the organization. This latest airship embodied in its construction many of the ideas of the late Count Zeppelin.

Russia is making strenuous efforts to develop a tremendous air power. All over the Soviet Republic will be seen signs and propaganda to the effect that the future of Russia lies in the air. Under a department of aviation, with a minister, or commissar, at its head, agents go everywhere, organizing clubs called The Friends of Aircraft and Chemical Warfare. Airplanes visit these organizations and take up their members for flights and tell them what aviation holds for Russia. This propaganda is even disseminated through the Arctic among the Eskimos, Laplanders and inhabitants of Arctic Siberia to the shores of the Pacific; south to the Sea of Aral and Turkestan, the Caspian Sea, the Caucasus and the Crimea. The people respond energetically to this propaganda by liberal contributions to the Russian air force.

The Russians know that no invasion of their country can be made in the face of a strong air force. They also know that the only way of attacking their country and smashing up their few centers of population, destroying the fields and livestock, is through the air. No outside nation has ever conquered Russia, with the exception of Jenghiz Khan's armies, which, with their lightning movements and encircling attacks, were almost like aircraft, compared to the unwieldy armies of those days.

Their air power is organized into an air force with squadrons, groups, wings and brigades, of bombardment and pursuit aviation. Their vast armies are supplied with observation aviation. They have bought airplanes from every country that would sell to them. They are organizing their factories and make some very good planes.

Russian civil aviation has passenger lines radiating from Moscow to Germany and other points in Western Europe, and north to the White Sea in the Arctic, east across Asiatic Russian and Siberia to Vladivostock on the Pacific, also through Mongolia and to Peking, China. Aircraft fly to the south through the Caucasus into Turkestan and to the great city of Samarkand, once the capital of Tamerlane. Through all these vast areas, where only a short time ago the fastest means of transport was by camel or horse, dog or reindeer, the airplane wings its way, filled with passengers clothed with furs in the north, or with bright-colored turbans and silk robes in the south.

Russia labors under a great handicap because her industrial resources and factories are very limited, as are her technicians and mechanics, but she is trying to overcome this by strenuous work and careful education. Russia's department of aviation is organized similarly to the others, with military and civil departments and a department of experimentation. At present, Russia has about 1200 airplanes under the colors.

Japan began her aeronautic development shortly after the war. Seeing the tremendous effect which aircraft were having on the conduct of war, she put out redoubled efforts, particularly after the bombardment experiments carried out in the United States in 1921 had proved beyond a doubt that battleships are at the mercy of air power. They obtained French instructors to organize their land aviation and British instructors for their aviation with the navy. They bought the best models of aircraft they could get from France, Great Britain, Italy and Germany, then established their own factories for making them. As there were no automobile factories in Japan, it was quite a job to get the motor industry started. Gradually they have evolved a powerful air force, their system being based on that of the French. Their army has been cut down and the money saved from this put into the air force. They are moving toward a department of aviation along the lines followed in Europe. The small islands in the vicinity of Japan have been organized so that air forces can land on them. If any navy attempted to cross the Pacific from America or from the north or south, they would most assuredly be attacked far out at sea by the Japanese air force and destroyed.

The Japanese make excellent aviators. Naturally at first they were entirely unaccustomed to going into the air and had not served their apprenticeship of years, like Americans and Europeans, in developing the airplane. Some thought, as they did not do everything at once, that they would never make good aviators, but that is not the case. They are athletic, quick of eye and thought, brave and resourceful, self-reliant and enduring, and these are the very qualities that make good flyers. As Japan, above all else, is a military nation, they can be trusted to develop their aviation to the utmost, and in a sensible manner. They have about 1500 airplanes with the colors at present.

The kingdom of Siam, the last absolute monarchy in the world except that of Sarawak, in Borneo, has a department of aviation and an independent air force. This air force, though small, is active and well organized, and flies all over the country, affording protection to its frontiers and a means of communication to outlying districts. It does a great deal of sanitary work, such as carrying doctors to various places and bringing patients who have been injured, fallen sick or been bitten by venomous reptiles, into the hospitals at Bangkok. The Siamese make fine aviators. They send aviation students to schools in Europe and America, and are thoroughly conversant with the world's aeronautical progress.

The Dutch in Java maintain a considerable air force. Few people realize that the Dutch empire in the East Indies consists of 55,000,000 people, industrious and great agriculturists, who have made of these islands one of the great garden spots of the world. The air force is exceptionally well organized, with splendid officers and fine mechanics and very good airplanes. A force of about 300 planes is used to handle any native uprisings, patrol

General and Mrs. Mitchell Visiting the Siamese Air Force in Bangkok

Part of America's Last Air Force Assembled at Langley Field in 1921

the coasts, map the islands and their coast lines, effect communication between their multitude of islands, carry officials on inspection trips and aid commercial development, prospecting for oil, timber and fisheries.

Even China, rent asunder by the terrible civil wars that have been progressing there for many years, takes a great interest in aviation. Her people have got over the feeling that the airplane is the "white man's devil." So far, on account of the great instability of their government, they have been able to do very little in a positive way.

The South American states are all interested in aviation and are developing it in accordance with their needs, using it for military purposes and for the transportation of passengers, express and mail.

All over the world, aviation is taking its place as a major activity of the governments, organized in each into a department by itself which is on an equal basis with any other government department, and with a minister or cabinet member at its head. In all these countries it is more popular than the old army or navy services. The only great country in which this condition does not exist is the United States. Here the air activities are distributed between the War Department, Navy, Commerce, Treasury and Post Office Departments and other organizations, political or financial, that want to use aviation as a football. It is a disgraceful condition to contemplate. We have no air force worthy of the name and our commercial aviation is very poor. The great number of accidents that are occurring is a by-product of such a state of affairs.

The American people make the best pilots in the world. Our industries are more capable of turning out excellent airplanes than those of any other country, and we have every raw material necessary for the construction and upkeep of aircraft. America should lead the world in the air, and very easily can under an intelligent and educated leadership, but under present conditions nothing can be hoped for until a department of aviation is established.

BARLING BOMBER IN FLIGHT

THE BARLING BOMBER, THE LARGEST PRACTICAL AIRPLANE EVER BUILT IN THE UNITED STATES. IT HAD 2400 H.P. AND A LIFTING CAPACITY OF SIXTEEN TONS. IT COULD EASILY CARRY FIFTY MEN

CHAPTER XVII

MILITARY AVIATION

MILITARY aviation is that part of the national defense which relates to the prosecution of military campaigns by air. Nothing in the world's history has brought about as great a change in the employment of military power as the coming of the airplane.

War is the attempt of one nation to impress its will on another nation by force after all other means of arriving at an adjustment of a dispute have failed. The attempt of one combatant, therefore, is to so control the vital centers of the other that it will be powerless to defend itself. The vital centers consist of cities where the people live, areas where their food and supplies are produced and the transportation lines that carry these supplies from place to place.

From the dawn of history, nations have put numbers of men into the field, called armies, and launched them at these hostile centers. The opposing nation then put a wall of men in front of these places to defend them, and a combat took place to determine which side would gain the mastery. Gradually the theory grew up that the object of war was to destroy the hostile army in the field, because if this were done the country lay open to the invader. But the development of firearms has progressed to such a point that an army is no longer able to advance rapidly across the ground. One man entrenched with a modern machine gun can hold off forty or fifty coming against him.

In the Civil War, the Union and Confederate armies fought each other for four years between Washington and Richmond, Virginia, a distance of only 121 miles. In the World War, the armies in northern France fought for four and one half years, going backward and forward only about sixty miles after they had come into contact. Men were killed by the thousands, by machine gun fire, they were shot up with cannon, stuck with bayonets and devoured by disease. This modern and "humane" warfare could only result in one thing, the utter destruction of all the participants to such a combat. It ceased to be war and was merely a slaughterhouse performance in which no science, art or ingenuity was involved. The European war, except for a few battles at the beginning, was one of the most uninteresting that history records. Every part of the country and every activity of men, women and children was given over to maintaining the armies in the field. The countries had again swung back to the ancient system of the "nation in arms." In ancient days when a city was assaulted, every living creature within its walls assisted in the defense.

During the Middle Ages, a set of rules grew up where mercenary armies were employed to do the fighting. Often the combat of a few champions would determine the outcome of the battle. Of course this was readily upset when somebody disregarded the rules and did something new, thereby winning the victory. Armies have now fallen into much the same condition. They know no other method except to obtain more firearms and greater rapidity of fire, which requires an ever expanding system of supply.

The advent of air power which can go straight to the vital centers and entirely neutralize or destroy them has put a completely new complexion on the old system of making war. It is now realized that the hostile main army in the field is a false objective and the real objectives are the vital centers. The old theory, that victory meant the destruction of the hostile main army, is untenable. Armies themselves can be disregarded by air power if a rapid stroke is made against the opposing centers, because a greatly superior army numerically is at the mercy of an air force inferior in numbers. There is no place on the world's surface that aircraft cannot go. They can easily fly from America to Europe and back, with military loads, or from Asia to America and back.

The result of warfare by air will be to bring about quick decisions. Superior air power will cause such havoc, or the threat of such havoc, in the opposing country that a long drawn out campaign will be impossible. A country strong in the air and with means of radio communication, whereby one can talk to any place in the world with the speed of light, may very easily establish world dominion. Not only can a decisive stroke be made against a great industrial and commercial country by aircraft, but it can be held in subjection much more easily by an air force than by an army or navy. If insurrections or uprisings occur, aircraft are able to destroy the crops and render the fields infertile, kill the domestic animals, and of course destroy the dwellings, factories and storehouses by dropping gas or explosives. In this way a comparatively few men, using the most powerful instruments of warfare ever known, can control great areas.

The conceptions we have always had that wars must be waged by armies and navies must be revised, as these two branches of the military service will take a position second to that of air power, and

MILITARY AVIATION will act principally as aids to it. Armies will hold the land. Navies will no longer be able to remain on top of the water where they are a sure prey to aircraft, but will have to act in submarines beneath the surface. These submarines will really be an auxiliary of air power, helping it accomplish its missions by guiding aircraft across large water areas by radio signals, supplying them when they land on islands, picking them up when they are forced to land in the water. Submarines may even carry airplanes and put them out to give additional fuel or supplies to aircraft passing overhead.

Let us suppose that war occurs between a nation on a continent such as Europe, and one situated on an island or series of islands, such as England or Japan. Both these empires depend almost entirely for their existence on their overseas commerce. As most of their people have been called into the industrial centers to manufacture goods which they sell, there are very few left for the production of food and the necessities of life.

Great Britain is a direct descendant of the Phoenician system. This comprises a series of armed ports throughout the world into which the raw materials of the various countries are gathered. These materials are picked up by boats and transported to Great Britain where they are manufactured into articles of trade and then distributed to the world from ships. To break down these trade routes at any place, for instance, through the Mediterranean and the Suez Canal, would be her downfall. Just as the breakdown of the trade routes through the China Sea and the Straits of Malacca would have a corresponding effect on Japan.

Air power is entirely capable of breaking down these lines of communication by sinking the ships and causing the evacuation of the ports. An attack by air power on islands such as those comprising Great Britain and Japan would be decisive because the people have no place to go and nowhere to get food except on these comparatively small stretches of land. It is doubtful if a two months' reserve supply of food exists in Great Britain. The targets are well defined, easy to pick up and hit. Both these nations thoroughly realize this and have both organized great air forces which are entirely independent of the army and navy, and are charged specifically with the defense of all the air over their respective countries and with making air attacks against enemy countries.

In all the leading countries, air, land and water are under independent ministries, which are brought into one organization, either a department of national defense with a secretary or minister at its

MILITARY AVIATION

head, or under a committee that handles the war making system of the state. In this way coordination is secured and each branch of the service has its own voice in the plans and arrangements.

In England, the Air Commander has charge of all defense arrangements for the British Isles in case of war, and the actions of the army and navy within 200 miles of the coast will be coordinated under his direction. In other words, the head airman is the supreme commander of all forces in case England is attacked.

I mention England particularly, because they received very heavy casualties and damages from aircraft bombs during the war, which brought home to them what would happen in another war. England started in the World War with an army air service and a navy air service, just as we have in the United States now. When the German airplanes raided England, the Army air service would chase them to the shores of the sea, at which point they would have to turn around and go back. The navy air service was then supposed to take up the pursuit, but they were never there, so the result was that the Germans got safely away. The British soon put a stop to this state of affairs by creating a Ministry and an Independent Air Force.

In the United States today, there is an indescribable mess about the defense arrangements all along our coast and in the interior. Nobody knows who has charge of anything. There is no air commander and no similarity of instruction between the air services of the Army, Navy, Marines or Coast Guard. If we had a well organized air force, entirely independent of the army and navy, no ship could approach our coasts across the Atlantic or Pacific Oceans. The air force is the only thing that can go up in the air and fight hostile aircraft. It is the only force that can launch an attack against a foreign country, either north or south of us, or across the oceans.

The stepping stones across the Atlantic are not as far apart as most people think. Going by way of Labrador, Greenland, Iceland and Scandinavia, or the various islands north of Great Britain, the greatest sea hop is less than 500 miles.

An even closer bridge exists to Asia. There are only 52 miles of water separating Alaska from Siberia. It is along these lines that future invasions will come because they are the shortest lines and aircraft will fly direct along them, using comparatively small islands for their bases of operations, and strike directly at the great vital centers.

The United States is the most continuously self-contained country that the world has ever seen. In case of war, it can easily exist without ocean borne commerce. We raise everything that is absolutely essential to our maintenance and supply. Therefore, even if a Navy were effective as a means of controlling the seas, it would have comparatively little influence with us because we can very easily get along without it. Countries such as England or Japan are unalterably tied to their sea lanes of communication for existence. We in this country are least tied to them of any nation on earth.

Future wars will see aircraft used in great units, employed in much the same manner as regiments and brigades in an army. In the World War, at the battle of St. Mihiel, I had 1476 airplanes available for combat. The Germans were confined to a salient, an angle running into our position. I so timed the attacks of our planes that several hundred would hit from the right side of the salient and then several hundred from the left side. As soon as the combat became general, the main attack was launched by aircraft which had flown clear around both forces and attacked the enemy in the rear. This is the kind of strategy that will be exercised in future. The air attack will come from whatever direction offers the greatest advantage to the attacker. He has the whole air to operate in. He has radio to use from plane to plane, and from plane to ground stations, which enables him to communicate anywhere he desires. He can use the greatest weapons of all time and can bring about decisions in warfare with a speed never conceived of before. Once the power of initiative is seized by an air force, the opponent had better make peace.

All our old conceptions of armies, navies and military strategy have to be changed, so great has the influence of air power become. It is a distinct move for the betterment of civilization, because wars will be decided quickly and not drag on for years. What will future war hold for us? Undoubtedly an attack on the great centers of population. If a European country attacks the United States, New York, Chicago, Detroit, Pittsburgh and Washington will be the first targets. It is unnecessary that these cities be destroyed in the sense that every house be levelled with the ground. It will be sufficient to have the civilian population driven out of them so that they cannot carry on their usual vocations. A few gas bombs will do that.

Picture what the dropping of a gas bomb will mean. Two thousand pounds of liquid gas smashes down in a street. None of the defending forces on the ground have even heard the airplane. It may be miles off, and may have released a gliding bomb when ten or fifteen miles away; or an air torpedo,

A Construction Representing the Skyline of a City Being Bombed by Airplanes

Smoke Curtain Over New York Laid by an Airplane Showing How Gas Curtains Can Be Laid Which Will Drift Over Large Cities for Twenty or Thirty Minutes

A Smoke or Gas Curtain Being Laid to Cover a Warship

MILITARY AVIATION

which may be fired at a range of 100 miles or more. This great concentration of gas surges along, entering the lower stories of buildings. Men, women and children come rushing out and fall dead in the streets. Gradually it reaches the upper stories and suffocates those who have stayed inside. The accumulation of gas may be so great that no gas mask will protect against it. The news spreads everywhere of what has happened and just as this comes home to the people, a second bomb of the same size or larger hits in another place, then another and another. There is a wild and disorderly exodus from the city for the outlying fields and forests, where there are no tents or houses for the refugees. The hundreds of thousands from the great cities cannot be fed. Railroads and motor trucks attempt to bring in provisions but the principal bridges on the high roads have been broken down by the attack of aircraft. The people are helpless. There is only one alternative and that is surrender. It is a quick way of deciding a war and really much more humane than the present methods of blowing people to bits by cannon projectiles or butchering them with bayonets.

Airplanes have flown across the oceans, airships have traveled around the world, and naturally people must be convinced by this time that attacks such as I have described are quite possible. Men and nations still have differences and as long as these differences exist, they will be magnified and result in war. Those who stick to the old systems of armies and navies and do not utilize air power to its fullest extent are the ones who will be beaten.

We hear a great deal in these days about the necessity for navies, and what they can do. Navies have never been anything except an auxiliary of armies in their rôle of controlling communications across the water. A boat is one of the most vulnerable objects known for aircraft attack. There are three conditions involved in an attack on seacraft. One is finding them. Aircraft, from their position on high, afford a clearer and wider vision than that obtainable on any seacraft. If the weather is thick or cloudy, men on ships can see nothing but the man in the airplane can see a great deal. Consequently, the problem of search and location of hostile seacraft is a comparatively easy one for aircraft. Vessels on the water are very inefficient as far as finding other seacraft is concerned.

The next problem is that of approach. We found out a great deal about this during the World War. Anti-aircraft artillery and any means of defense from the ground against the air is futile. Of the air force under my command, less than one tenth of

Four Twenty-Five-Pound Bombs Hitting Ship

Thirty Seconds After the Four Twenty-Five-Pound Phosphorous Bombs Hit the Battleship

The Battleship as She Appeared as the Bomb Hit Her

Battleship After Being Hit by an Eleven-Hundred-Pound High Explosive Bomb

one percent were lost from the action of anti-aircraft artillery or the fire of missile throwing weapons from the ground, and in that case the aircraft were acting very close to the ground, tied up to armies in reconnaissance work, in the adjustment of fire for the artillery and directly attacking hostile troops on the ground. There is no point in the air against which anti-aircraft artillery may be ranged, such as there is on the ground where the burst of projectiles may be watched with reference to a tree on a distant hill, or a church steeple, a road or other prominent physical feature. On the water, one may watch the splash where the projectile hits. But the airplane is going at a tremendous rate of speed, constantly changing altitude and direction. In addition, if the anti-aircraft defenses amount to anything, low flying airplanes directly attack them, covering the batteries with gas or smoke, so that the people on the ground are completely at a loss, and do not know what is going on.

A battleship's capacity for carrying anti-aircraft machine guns and cannon is quite limited. If one wanted to develop as much fire against aircraft from a battleship as from a single regiment of infantry, the guns would have to be planted so thickly on it that it would look like a hair brush.

The third problem is that of destroying the ship or putting it out of action. Shipping may be attacked by gas. Gas clouds ejected by airplanes can completely envelop a fleet which cannot get away from them. The ventilating systems in ships suck the gas right into their interiors. Even if gas masks are put on the outside of the ventilators and every member of the crew wears a mask, such a great concentration of gas can be made that no one can escape its effects. Picture the plight of a crew under a gas attack when a heavy sea is running. The hostile airplanes approach and lay a succession of gas curtains surrounding the fleet. The crews put on their masks which they dare not take off as the gas pervades the ship. The heat is intense and they become seasick inside the masks, then it is a question of taking them off or smothering. In a short time, the ship is entirely at the mercy of aircraft.

In addition to gas, there are many other weapons. The automobile torpedo fired from aircraft has a range of four or five miles. It is discharged close to the water where it is almost impossible to be seen from a battleship, particularly if a diversion by aircraft is made in another direction. Attack by explosive bombs has been proved to be entirely effective in crippling and sinking the largest and strong-

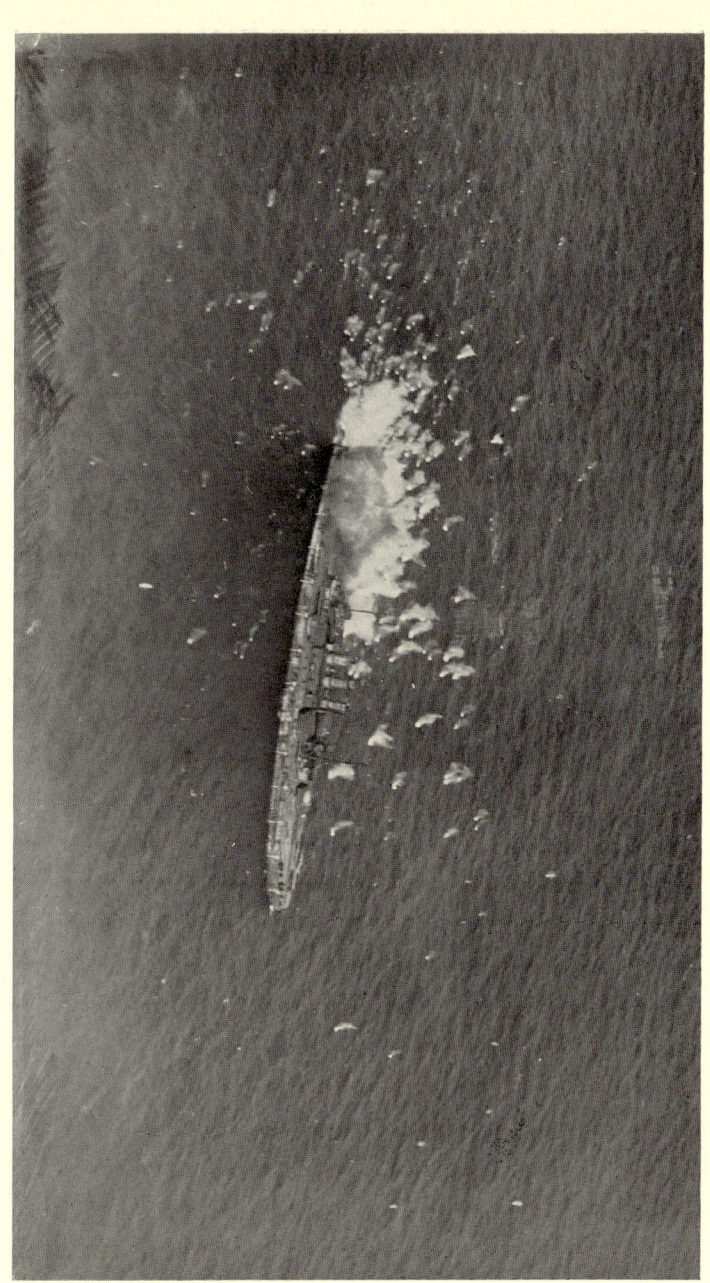

Direct Hit by an Eleven-Hundred-Pound Bomb on a Battleship

A Four-Thousand-Pound Bomb, the Greatest Weapon Produced by Man

est ships that can be built. These weapons are the greatest that man has ever devised, on account of their explosive content. An ordinary projectile from a cannon carries only from five to fifteen percent of its total weight in explosive. The armor piercing projectiles of naval cannon contain even less, a two thousand pound armor-piercing projectile from a 16 inch gun carrying about sixty pounds of TNT. An air bomb, however, that weighs a ton carries anywhere from 1100 to 1500 pounds of TNT. If this projectile hits in the vicinity of a ship, within a couple of hundred feet, the underwater mining effect or "water hammer" is so great that it will cave in the bottom of the ship, causing it to sink.

If a person puts his hand into water, the water feels soft. If he slaps it, it will feel a little harder; but if he strikes with great force, it can split his hand open. If you detonate a great mass of high explosive under water, it will throw the water against the ship with such velocity that the effect will be the same as throwing a mass of steel. Not only that, but as the water pervades every nook and crevice, it will get into the pipes leading to the condensers, bend the rudders, propellors and even their shafts.

Not only may projectiles be launched at battleships by the ordinary system of dropping bombs when the airplane is overhead but the plane can dive for its target at an angle and loose the bomb which will keep up its velocity along the same line that the airplane is flying, at any angle under forty five degrees.

A naval fleet spends the greater portion of its time in harbor and this is particularly so since the advent of the submarine. A fleet in a harbor is very vulnerable to air attack, even more so than when at sea, because they are congested in a small area. It offers a better target, being more concentrated, and the water is shallower. Bombs exploding against a bottom in shallow water have more effect than in deep water because the bottom acts like the breech of a cannon and projects most of their force upward.

Another great delusion which the Navyists attempt to foster is the airplane carrier. If it were merely a question of the operation of one fleet against another, the airplane carrier might do some good, but these tremendously costly structures are completely at the mercy of air forces acting from shore bases, because the airplane carrier can house and launch very few airplanes, three or four at a

MILITARY AVIATION

time and a maximum of sixty or seventy. These probably could never return intact because the landing space is not large enough for them to come down at one time. Air forces acting from shore stations would deploy several thousand airplanes against them in attacks. Therefore the value of the airplane carrier is largely mythical. These are some of the reasons why people in all countries are advocating an agreement on naval disarmament.

While surface seacraft are very easy for aircraft to destroy, the submarine is a different matter. When it is submerged, unless the water is very clear, it is almost impossible for the airplane to find it. Submarines remain hidden in the daytime at great depths and come to the surface at night. Not only can they use guns of any size, but also they can launch aerial torpedoes, directing them by radio against objects on land. Their effect against ocean borne shipping is tremendous. During the war they destroyed more than half of all Great Britain's commercial ships. In the future, they will be used to attack hostile commerce and will be employed as an auxiliary by the air forces as described above. The best defense against submarines are other submarines, and after that, aircraft.

In future wars, aircraft will project the spear point of the nation's offensive and defensive power

SKYWAYS

against the vital centers of the opposing country. Then woe be to the nation that is weak in the air. It will fall a prey to its enemy more quickly than has ever been the case in war waged by armies and navies.

CHAPTER XVIII

THE USE OF AIRCRAFT IN THE WAR

MILITARY aviation is divided into various arms of the service in a manner somewhat analogous to ground troops or navies. The basis of air force power is the bombardment airplane or bomber. These ships carry anywhere from one thousand to eight thousand pounds of military weapons, that is, explosive bombs, gas, incendiary and phosphorus bombs, gliding bombs, the air and water torpedo, and a means for laying toxic gas curtains. They can be equipped to lay contact or anchor mines in the sea, or across harbors. These bombers, from their size, weight and carrying ability, cannot be made to maneuver as rapidly as others, consequently they have to be protected either by their own gunfire or by swifter and more maneuverable airplanes.

Bombardment aviation is organized into squadrons, groups, wings or regiments, brigades and divisions. The basic unit is the squadron of about twenty-five airplanes. The group consists of three or four squadrons, the wing or regiment of three groups. Two or three wings form a brigade and two or three brigades form a division. Although we have never had any tactical corps of air force corresponding to the army corps, there undoubtedly will be an organization of this kind in the future. In some services, pursuit aviation, the branch with the greatest speed, maneuverability and gun power that is designed to fight other aircraft primarily, is brigaded or joined with bombardment aviation. That is, in a wing or regiment of air force, there may be two groups of pursuit aviation of one hundred airplanes each and one group of bombardment of one hundred airplanes; or there may be one group of pursuit and two groups of bombardment and so on into the higher units.

The command and staff system of air forces correspond to similar organizations on the ground or water. Each unit has its commander, its organization for gathering information, for getting out the orders and transmitting them to commanders for whose use they are intended. They have supply departments which keep up the food and clothing for the men, the fuel and repair parts for the airplanes and the means of transportation necessary for delivering these things to the air units. In future air units will be supplied largely by transport airplanes acting through the air because means of supply on the ground by automobile or railroad are not only slow but might not be able to reach the positions from which aircraft operate.

BOMBING PLANES IN ACTION
(*From the Painting by Lieutenant Melville of Captain Bissell's Attack Against the "Ostfriesland"*)

General Mitchell Beside a Pursuit Plane

AIRCRAFT IN WAR

There is a basic difference in the nature of combat indulged in by an air force as distinguished from an army or navy. In the army, the infantry soldier is the basis of organization. Everything else is built up on him. His officers are there primarily to handle him, put him into combat and have him direct his fire where it will do the most good. Artillery is placed around him to facilitate his advance and cavalry is assigned to watch over and protect him. With the air force, the soldier or enlisted man is a highly trained mechanic, having a knowledge of shop methods and machine tools, armament, weapons, optical instruments and photography and all sorts of engines and materials. These men are the most highly trained technically of any troops in any branch of the military service. Their care and supervision of airplanes and the responsibility attached to it requires that they be individuals of the highest order, that never make a mistake.

The pilots and observers who constitute the officer personnel are the ones who do the fighting, much as the knights did in the Middle Ages, attended by their men-at-arms, squires, grooms and lackeys. The result of this condition is a very close personal association between the flying officers and the enlisted men under them. An even more rigid discipline is required than is the case in the infantry or other branches of the ground service. The hours of duty are much longer for the enlisted airman, as he has to work on his airplane all night and all day when in active operations. He has to take care of the pilots, even putting them to bed, rubbing them, feeding them and treating them like delicate machines. If the pilot of an airplane has an efficient crew, the principal burden of his existence is removed from him and he steps into his airplane with nothing on his mind except his mission against the enemy. Some of the psychological phases of this relation are interesting.

The man who does the fighting in the air force is a very high order of human being. Whereas the attack is made by units larger than the individual plane, in the last analysis of a combat, it is the individual plane that closes with his adversary and fights him, either by the fire action of his guns or bombs and gas screens, or possibly, now that we have parachutes, by ramming. There is no one very close to support and talk to him or give him assistance, as there is with ground troops in an army. He is absolutely on his own. But also he cannot glance into the faces of his comrades and see the terror they express, and become imbued with panic which often seizes ground troops and causes their utter demoralization and destruction. We have never known such a thing as panic in an air force. While some individuals may be subject to it, there are always others who remain unaffected.

In the handling of air force units, a wide front or great distances between organizations is usually maintained, for two reasons. It offers a better defense against enemy bombardment, which always seeks to attack air forces while they are on the ground. Also, it is easier to launch an attack with air units placed far apart. The essence of air attack is to approach the objective from different directions so as to mislead the enemy, separate him into various detachments, maneuver him out of his position in the air, then combine one's own forces at the crucial moment where they will do the most good.

Pursuit aviation sometimes uses what are called surveillance airplanes to give information of what lies ahead. These are very swift craft equipped with radio telegraphy, which depend for their safety on extreme speed and ceiling. These ships report what they see by radio to the commanders of the air force. When the hostile pursuit is located, the approach is made with the greatest rapidity and every advantage taken to obtain altitude, work into the sun in the daytime and away from the moon at night and get the first punch in at the enemy, so as to disorganize his formations.

The theory of pursuit attack against hostile pursuit is to bring a completely surrounding or enveloping attack in three dimensions, that is, from up above both in front and rear, on the same plane and from underneath. The elements of each tactical unit of pursuit aviation are arranged accordingly. Each squadron has three flights of from five to seven planes. The leading flight may be the lowest, the second flight a little higher and to the right and the third still a little higher and to the left. The next squadron will be higher and to the right of the first, the third squadron higher and to the left of the second, and the fourth, acting as the last formed reserve of the group, with which the commander of the group takes his position, may be above all of them.

The attack of the group may commence by the leading flight of the first squadron flying straight into its adversary, maneuvering for position and delivering its fire. This is followed in fractions of a second by the other flights, then by the other squadron. By this time the mêlée is general, the fight resolving itself into combats of single individuals which spread out over a great extent of air, sometimes several miles apart. The commander of the

British Pursuit Airplane, the "Partridge"

British Single-Seater Pursuit Plane Called the "Bristol" Which Has a Speed of About 180 Miles per Hour and a Ceiling of 31,000 Feet

BOMBARDMENT SQUADRON IN FLIGHT

group launches his last squadron where its effect will be the greatest and success depends upon a leader's ability to gauge when to use his last formed unit, very much as it used to be in the old days of cavalry combat on the ground. Victory lies with the one who can be the last to fling his formed reserve into the fight.

Bombardment aviation flies in just as compact formations as possible, usually in a "V" like a flight of ducks or geese. In that formation, more effective control may be kept over all the ships. Also, a greater volume of controlled fire can be brought by a compact mass of large airplanes than by individuals. Bombardment airplanes have machine guns and cannon that will fire to the front, up or down, to the rear, up or down, and from either side. They are manned with crews of four or five men. Sometimes the crew is equipped with body armor or bullet proof clothing which will keep off 30-calibre machine gun projectiles or fragments of shell. In case of attack, the bombardment ships huddle together as closely as possible and if near the ground or water, they fly close to it so that the attacking airplanes cannot get under them, as the most dangerous attack against bombers is from beneath. Thus they are able to confine their adversary to two planes of attack, from above and on the level.

On the other hand, where they are engaged in long voyages to their objective, they fly as near ceiling as possible. In future this will be around 35,000 feet or higher. Crews will be equipped with oxygen gas and their engines with superchargers. At this high altitude, pursuit aviation will have difficulty in getting above them and will not be able to maneuver as easily in the thin air as lower down. Also, it will be difficult to find the bombardment planes in sufficient time for the enemy pursuit aviation to reach them.

Toward the end of the war in Europe, we had a great deal of experience in the use of an air force, and could see what its future possibilities and methods of handling might be. We had begun to bombard military establishments of the Germans in the cities along the Rhine, and had the war lasted until 1919, we would have carried the air war into the industrial districts of Essen and clear to Berlin. This phase of air force work is the one outstanding development that occurred in the European war. It is the thing that will bring about victory or defeat in future military contests.

Before the use of air power in this way, the airplanes were used merely as a service for the ground troops. They reconnoitered by eye and photograph a few miles in front of the armies' position and reported movements of troops and trains. At first, army commanders, knowing little about aviation, placed very little credence upon their reports, but within a short while, it was found that they were the only service that could bring in accurate reports quickly enough to counteract the swift movements by rail and motor car which were being used extensively. So fighting began in the air. Pursuit aviation was created, and later bombardment.

Toward the end of the war, a branch of aviation called "attack" was created for the purpose of attacking troops or other formations on the ground with machine gun fire and light bombs. The use of the machine gun against ground objectives or naval vessels has greatly increased since the war. At that time we only fired upon troops from two or three hundred yards. Now we get better results from larger machine guns and cannon at from two to five thousand yards. The airplane flies only a few feet above the ground when making its attack, protects itself by flying behind forests, hills or through ravines, or by getting close to the water where it is difficult to see. Much better practice can be made from machine guns in an airplane than from machine guns on the ground. This is because the guns in the plane have a recuperator or shock absorber of air all around the airplane. The jar from their discharge is practically all taken up, whereas on the ground, springs, oil buffers or air recuperators have to be used to deaden the shock against the hard earth, which deranges their aim much more than in the air.

This branch of aviation, however, will have most of its application in the future against what are termed partisan or irregular troops, such as are found in Asia or Africa, Mexico and Central America, that is, those not equipped with large air forces and which do not move in large numbers but in comparatively small mobile detachments. Attack aviation can also be used to disable or sink merchantmen or naval vessels up to the light cruiser.

Combat in the air is a gruelling contest for the individual. The strain on him physically and mentally and on his morale is terrific. The combat of the single seater ends invariably in the death of one of the contestants. No quarter is asked or given. On the other hand, more chivalry is displayed than in any other branch of a fighting service. To give an idea of what combat in the air is like, I take for an example the experience of a bombardment squadron under my command at the battle of St. Mihiel. His squadron failed to meet its escort of pursuit aviation at the appointed time and place, with the result that the enemy's pursuit attacked him unhindered. There were 18 airplanes in the squadron, fifteen being 2-seaters and three of them being 3-seaters. The 3-seaters were equipped with six guns each, and as far as volume of gunfire was concerned, were the most powerful airplanes on the European front. They were unable to maneuver as rapidly as the single seaters, however, and therefore did not fulfil the ideas of their originators who thought that through volume of fire alone they could defend themselves against small, highly maneuverable single seaters. The 3-seaters were supposed to be for the protection of the 2-seaters, that is, these powerfully gunned airplanes were expected to fight off the enemy pursuit while the bombers they were protecting could concentrate their whole attention on dropping their bombs on the targets.

The squadron flew in a V formation, one of the great 3-seaters being on each flank and one in the opening behind. When this squadron crossed the line on the way to its objective, it was passed by a patrol of twelve German pursuit airplanes flying one behind the other about 500 meters above it. The German patrol deployed in line formation behind the bombardment squadron. Four of the enemy airplanes attacked the 3-seater which was behind and sent it down in flames. The other eight kept up a long range fire at the squadron so as to derange its aim while dropping its bombs on the city of Conflans. At the same time, anti-aircraft artillery opened fire at the vanguard of the squadron while the German pursuit ships attacked the rear. While anti-aircraft guns failed to hit any of the airplanes their bursting shells allowed the German pursuit organizations, which were now concentrating for an attack on the squadron, to see where they were. During this time, the Commander of the bombardment squadron noticed German airplanes rising from the airdrome close to Conflans, that is, at Mars la Tour. The bombs were all dropped on the objective and the return flight was started to our own lines. Just as the turn was made, a fresh enemy pursuit squadron joined the former, immediately deployed and attacked the rearmost plane and shot the observer through the leg. He continued the battle, however, and hit one enemy plane which fell in flames. The formation was now well on its way back when a third enemy squadron attacked ours in front and to the left. The bombing squadron was now being attacked in three dimensions, from underneath, up above and on the same level.

To one who has never seen a fight of this kind, it is impossible to convey an idea with mere words. The great lumbering bombing machines huddled together as a flight of geese might when attacked by falcons. The pursuit airplanes diving at them from all directions, firing their machine guns, then zooming up in the air or turning over on their backs at a speed of about 200 miles an hour, taking an erratic course to avoid the fire of the big ships and then resuming their position for attack again. Frequently an airplane is hit, bursting into flames, losing a wing, or having its controls shot to pieces, or its pilot is killed instantly, when it spins away on its course to the ground, leaving a long trail of flame and black smoke behind it.

By this time the big 3-seater protection plane on the left had been shot in one of its engines and started slipping down. Immediately when it left the formation it was jumped on by three German machines. In a moment it was shot to pieces and disappeared in flames. Fighting now had become terrific. More German machines were constantly joining their comrades. The signals made by the artillery projectiles bursting in the air and the radio on the ground told the German aviators that our bombardment squadron had no pursuit protection and was an easy victim. The attacks of the German pursuit ships were carried on, up to within 50 feet of the bombardment planes. The next airplane to be hit was No. 13; the 2-seater caught fire and dropped its movable gasoline tank. It dived at a sharp angle, turned over on its back about 200 meters below the squadron, lost its left wing and then crashed to the ground. At the same moment a German pursuit ship was shot down on fire. No. 2 bombardment airplane was hit in the gasoline tank in the upper wing and caught fire, but the machine flaming like a torch kept its position in the formation. The machine gunner was magnificent in his courage, fighting the hostile airplane while the flames slowly crept around him. The plane continued to fly for about 200 meters, leaving behind it a trail of fire about twice as long as the ship itself. Pilot and observer by this time were consumed and the airplane dived to its doom. At about that time a German Fokker plane diving vertically with its engine full on, lost both its wings. Now the whole right wing of the squadron had been shot down and a rearrangement of formation was made so as to again get the remaining machines into a V formation. Machines Nos. 9 and 14 were then both hit at the same time, No. 14 catching fire. The pilot of No. 14 stretched out his arms toward the sky, and waving his hand and saying farewell to the remainder of the squadron, went to eternity. No. 9 machine disappeared, and as it did so an additional German pursuit machine retired from the combat crippled. No. 15 machine was now having a hard time keeping up with the formation. Its gasoline tank had been perforated by bullets, its aileron control cut and its rudder hit. However, it kept up.

By this time the squadron had come back to our lines and was joined and protected by our pursuit aviation. The combat in its intensity lasted for 40 minutes, and of eighteen airplanes which had constituted the squadron, only five remained. Most of the crews were wounded and their planes perforated in all parts by bullets. They had never once broken their formation nor failed to obey the orders of their leader.

During the war, what might be termed a branch of aviation was used for the defense of vital areas against aircraft. This system was brought to a particularly high state of efficiency in the vicinity of London and Paris. At first the defense was entrusted to the army which placed machine guns, anti-aircraft artillery and searchlights at points near the cities, totally neglecting defense by airplane or the establishment of observation and reporting stations far away from the city. Gradually these elements were unified and the responsibility for the whole air defense devolved upon the air force which placed one man in charge, who coordinated every part and branch, such as airplanes, observing posts, listening stations, searchlights, anti-aircraft artillery, nets raised in the air by balloons, balloons holding up cables to form barrages, and radio systems. There was a central electrical control system for the area which would tell on an illuminated board that represented a map of the whole terrain to be defended where hostile airplanes or airships were and where it was expected they would go. Each important post had a duplicate map. By this system, if a German airplane started to fly across the English Channel, it was reported by a station on an airplane, airship, a lightship, a submarine, a naval vessel, or by one of the coast guard stations along the shore. These were all equipped with listening devices for aircraft. Some stations even had cages of pheasants whose inner ear is very susceptible to any sound. They would fidget around and indicate the approach of an airplane or airship long before it could be detected by the human ear.

As the hostile airplanes approached more closely, the defense would send airplanes into the air over certain districts, at night as well as in the daytime. Searchlights were arranged to illuminate certain areas and other lights were held in reserve so as to trace the plane after the fixed lights had picked it up. This worked occasionally.

The balloon barrages or nets raised by balloons up to about 10,000 feet were feared by the aviators, but a means of cutting the cables from an airplane was devised, as well as shooting down the balloons. Other areas were covered by the fire of anti-aircraft artillery which formed a barrage in the air through which an airplane was supposed to be in danger, but very few airplanes were hit by this fire. The whole scheme, however, resulted in greatly diminishing air raids. It was almost entirely due to the effect of pursuit aviation which the defending forces had and not to the searchlights or anti-aircraft artillery.

Just before the Armistice I inaugurated a system of this kind along the front of the American Army to guard against attack by the heavy Gotha airplanes. It was only in effect three days before the Armistice but during that time our night pursuit had five combats with the Gothas and either succeeded in driving them off or in so interfering with their operations that they had to leave.

Our best defense against the German bombardment was to keep bombing their airdromes. At the time of the Armistice, out of forty of their largest airplanes acting against our front, only about six were fit for duty, the others being smashed up or injured. They would start off from one airdrome and land at another because we would follow them back and when they turned the lights on to land, we would attack them on the ground. This was a page out of the German's book, however. One night on the Ochey airdrome, just behind Toul, where there was a group of English Handley-Page bombers of the largest type, a German Gotha followed a British ship in, watched it make its signal for landing, waited a little while and then made the same signal, whereupon the landing lights were turned on again. The German ship came down within a couple of hundred feet and bombed it, hitting every hangar in the place, and completely destroying twenty-four Handley-Page and other airplanes. The whole group was put out of commission by this one attack.

In the future, defenses against aircraft along somewhat similar lines will be established except that the reporting posts will consist of dirigible airships equipped as airplane carriers and assisted by submarines, which will be stationed a thousand miles or more away from the vital centers. When the positions of any attacking formations are discovered, these airships will launch their airplanes against them, reporting by radio, and attempt to

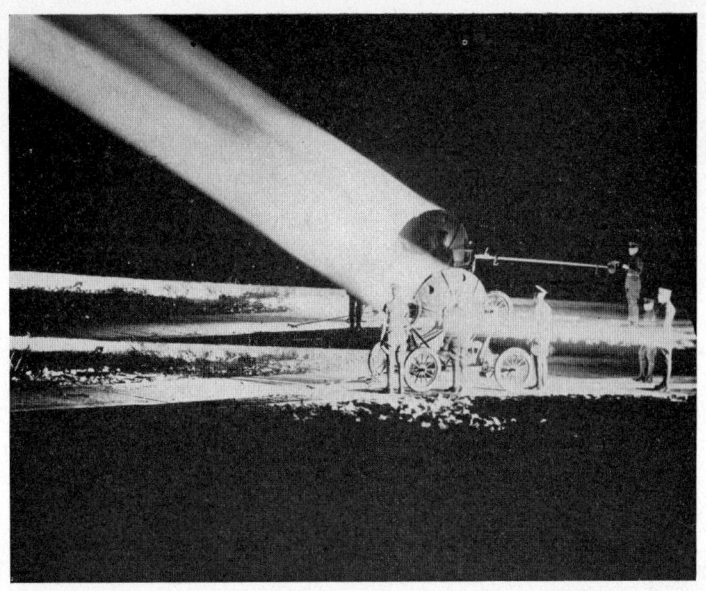

ANTI-AIRCRAFT SEARCHLIGHTS USED TO ILLUMINATE PLACES SUBJECT TO AIRCRAFT ATTACK

MODERN ANTI-AIRCRAFT BATTERY BEING PUT IN POSITION

Four Dirigible Airships in Formation Over Langley Field

AIRCRAFT IN WAR

hinder the advance of the opposing air forces. Airplanes of the future will be practically noiseless and it will be impossible to pick them up by listening devices. It is a serious question whether any defense against attacking aircraft will be efficient, so great is their power of concealment in the vast spaces of the air.

In future wars, it will be too late to organize an air force after the contest begins because the one who gets the first crack in against the hostile cities and vital points will have a tremendous advantage, not only in demolishing those places but in sweeping the air of his adversary because the other will have to attack in a piecemeal manner, as the organization of his air units is completed, and without a large concentrated force. Every airplane that a nation owns, whether commercial, civil or military, is a great asset, as they can all be used in an emergency.

CHAPTER XIX

AERONAUTICAL LAW

The coming of air transportation into regularly organized passenger, mail and freight services required that a complete new set of laws be formulated for the regulation of this kind of travel. These had to be applied in several different ways; first, the public had to be safeguarded by requiring that the aircraft in which they travelled be safe, that the pilots flying them be well instructed and competent, that the mechanics who worked on the planes be efficient and careful, that the airdromes and fields be suitable and safe for the handling of aircraft, that the airways be well marked and provided with suitable facilities in case of forced landings away from the airports, and that good weather reporting and forecasting systems, and radio, be provided.

Regulations were drawn up in somewhat the same manner as those which apply to vessels on the sea, their inspection, the condition of the equipment and crews. Some humorous incidents turned up in the early promulgation of these rules. The British Board of Trade, which is something like our Department of Commerce, was at first charged with the management of civil aviation. They enacted a regulation that when two aircraft going in opposite directions met in a fog they should blow their foghorns!

A totally new condition arose, which concerned the rights and liabilities of the companies operating aircraft, of the pilots flying them, the passengers travelling in them, and the rights of the property owners over whose land the airplanes flew. According to the common law, a man owns all the air above his property and all the ground under it to the center of the earth. Obviously, however, it is not to the public interest to have any property owner "post" or restrict flying over his property. On the other hand, regulations have to protect him against being molested in his occupation by airplanes which might fly too low or otherwise constitute a nuisance. If an airplane crashed on a house, setting it on fire, the liability for such an occurrence had to be fixed. If the owner of property erected a high tower which was unlighted at night, without notifying the authorities who regulated air traffic in that vicinity, and an airplane crashed into it, killing all the passengers and destroying the plane, who would be liable for that? A great number of such questions arose, for which there was no precedent in law.

Of the two conditions, that relating to the control of the traffic itself required a special court and magistrates to try cases resulting from infractions of the regulations. The civil courts have to do with determining the damages that might be inflicted on a property owner by an airplane and its occupants, or by a property owner to an airplane and its occupants. The status of an airplane as a common carrier had to be carefully defined so that capital would be encouraged to invest in it, so that insurance companies would have sufficient data to write insurance, and passengers would have some protection in case they were injured, their baggage lost or the trips not concluded as agreed upon.

Another important phase of air transportation relates to international communication by aircraft. The same two problems appear, but in a broader and more complicated phase. To begin with, each country required a certain licensing arrangement for its aircraft, and would not necessarily recognize the license of foreign craft. Eventually certain nations who had been allies during the war had an international convention on this subject and uniform rules were adopted. Each nation that was a signatory to this agreement recognized the licensing arrangement of the others. It was provided that foreign aircraft should land in specified ports of entry, where the passengers could show their passports, be examined as to health, and have their baggage inspected by customs officials. The airplane's manifest could be looked at, just the way steamship travel is regulated. If the airplane was forced to land at a place other than a port of entry, its pilot was required to report to the nearest government station, upon which it was incumbent to extend police protection and assistance to the airplane until repairs were effected or other disposition was made of it.

If a French airplane flying over Germany had a forced landing and crashed into a German brewery, smashing up the building and machinery, would the amount of damages due be adjudicated in the German or French courts? Such cases have followed in general the laws recognized in admiralty procedure, based on similar cases in maritime traffic.

Some other new aspects presented themselves in regard to air traffic. An airplane might photograph defensive works and fortifications, throw out revolutionary propaganda in a foreign country, or land undesirable aliens. Each of these cases is handled by certain courts according to the police power of the state, and adjudicated according to their merits. Sometimes the airplane is liable to seizure and its crews to imprisonment. If the country from which they came has been lax in its enforcement of neutrality or friendly relations, it is liable to damages from a diplomatic standpoint. Filibustering or transportation of arms and military equipment and the transfer of fighting airplanes themselves from one country to another has taken place, which involves additional questions.

These conditions led to further conferences, particularly between European nations that were close neighbors, with the result that these matters are regulated. There are certain areas over which foreign airplanes may not fly, and the use of cameras from aircraft is prohibited in certain places. These rules are published and given wide circulation so that any companies operating aircraft may become familiar with them.

In the United States, we have somewhat different conditions from those that exist in Europe. According to our Constitution, the Federal government is empowered to carry out certain rules and regulations which concern the whole people, and the states have jurisdiction over everything not specifically ceded to the Federal government. It has been determined in the case of railways and coastwise shipping that the Federal government has the power to regulate traffic from one state to another, that is, interstate commerce, but within their own boundaries, the state governments are supreme.

AERONAUTICAL LAW

The United States passed an Air Commerce Act in 1926 which regulated air traffic between the states, provided for the inspection of aircraft, pilots, mechanics, airways, landing fields and weather services and the necessary adjuncts to air transportation. Later laws were passed authorizing the Department of Commerce to provide rules under which aeronautical schools would be inspected so that adequate flying instruction would be given. Each of the states however is free to regulate its own aeronautical conditions. Most of them now recognize the Federal system and licenses and are gradually developing a similar set of rules. Cases of damages and liability of the carriers and crews are being handled in the courts in a manner similar to those arising in older forms of transportation, with variations where the point is particularly applicable to air transport. In this manner an entirely new set of laws and regulations depending on them is being created to govern air transport.

From time to time, particularly when a new weapon of war is created, nations attempt to restrict its use, especially those nations with a preponderance of the old forms of defense, who are afraid they will be injured by the new ones. The knights in armor attempted to restrict the use of firearms as being inhumane. The great maritime powers attempt to restrict the use of submarines as being inhumane. They also attempt to restrict the use of gas and the action of aircraft. Naturally none of these restrictions will have much force in time of war, because these very instruments are the most effective. To make international rules and regulations of this kind effective, it would be necessary to have all the great nations of the earth comply with them, and their people consent to their provisions. If a great nation such as Russia or Germany were left out of it, all the proceedings would be nullified.

Heretofore, the nations have attempted to restrict the fighting between armies to a certain zone and what are called military objectives, such as forts, lines of communication and supply points in the immediate vicinity of armies. This area was regulated largely by the distance which the heaviest artillery was able to fire, a space of a few miles. The creation of the German long distance gun during the World War which fired 70 miles, and the ability of aircraft to bombard hostile objectives hundreds of miles away rudely interrupted the old system of war. An attempt therefore has been made by various conferences to define what a military objective is. It is now accepted that a great factory or railroad terminal is a military objective. But if an airplane drops a two thousand pound bomb on a factory or station in the center of a city, the deadly effect is felt half a mile all around. If the flyer wishes to drop a bomb somewhere else in the city, he can say that he was aiming his fire at the station or factory, and missed his target. It is evident that none of the prohibitions attempted against the use of new weapons will have any more effect than they did in the past.

There will grow up a set of rules for air blockades of districts that are important to the enemy. For instance, it is conceivable that if foreign nations attacked the United States, they would notify our government to immediately evacuate Manhattan Island on which New York stands, and both shores of the Hudson and East Rivers for a distance of ten miles around, or an air attack of explosive bombs and gas would be initiated and kept up. The same might apply to the districts around Philadelphia, Pittsburgh, Washington, Detroit and Chicago. Under these conditions, if the United States felt strong enough to resist an attack, it might continue to allow the cities to be occupied. If we did not and were faced with their evacuation or certain destruction, we might capitulate and pay a very large indemnity. We are faced therefore with a set of rules analogous to those applied to the attack of a fortified city by an army, in which a certain amount of time is given the inhabitants to surrender or evacuate their women, children and non-combatants before the city is turned over to artillery bombardment, its water supply cut off and the ingress of food stopped.

Aeronautical blockades will also be declared against shipping on the high seas which will involve questions even more serious than those brought up by the submarines, because aircraft ordinarily will have no means of searching the ship and examining her papers, or putting aboard a prize crew, or taking care of the passengers and crew in case the ship is sunk. It will be reasonable, however, under these circumstances for the aircraft to signal the captain of the ship to abandon it in his small boats and give them a certain number of minutes to do so, after which the vessel will be sunk.

Most people do not realize these things. Those in authority in countries that are very vulnerable to air attack or who have weak air forces attempt to evade these questions as long as they can, but they must be faced and regulated as far as possible by international agreements and conferences.

The coming of aircraft therefore will result in an entirely new jurisprudence which might be termed the law of the sky, as distinguished from the law of the land and the law of the sea.

CHAPTER XX

AVIATION OF THE FUTURE

AERONAUTICS is the world's most absorbing subject. To the practical minded, it offers the quickest means of transportation which we have ever known. To the man of science, it has other appeals. There is a possibility that by this means we may reach beyond our atmosphere into the unknown spaces, and go from one planet and celestial body to another. Aviation is merely in an embryonic state at present. We know that gravity, or the attraction of one molecule of matter for another, is modified by temperature. At the Absolute Zero, where all heat is absent (somewhere around 458 degrees below zero, Fahrenheit), there is no resistance whatever to the passage of an electric current. Already temperatures within 3 or 4 degrees of the Absolute Zero have been reached by the liquefication of helium. If we can transmit energy without resistance, and if we can apply the rocket principle of propulsion successfully to aircraft, they may go anywhere. There are substances such as radium which are constantly active within themselves, and if we could utilize them, we would have a constant source of power.

SKYWAYS

The problem of navigation anywhere in space is undergoing much careful study now. Hermetically sealed cabins have been built, which carried stores of compressed air and were provided with means for absorbing the poisons from the breath as it was exhaled. They had electrical controls, which obviated the necessity for holes or orifices in the cabin for sticks to manipulate the controls. I had a chamber of this kind constructed in 1921, which was successfully flown.

To some these ideas may seem to belong to the nebulous future, but they are no further away from us than the telephone, radio and electric light were from our fathers, or the airplane was from people who have now passed the half century mark. Those who develop aviation, or anything new for that matter, must not be bound by the traditions of the past. Creative developments occur in cycles. Certain schools of thought are started by individuals, the results of which are worked out to a certain stage, then there succeeds a lapse in creation, when the practical features of the thing are developed, put into use and standardized. Ordinarily, scientists and engineers do not initiate the new ideas, because they deal with exact facts. Science means exact knowledge. Creative ability causes a man to look beyond the established facts of today, and is quite inde-

FUTURE AVIATION

pendent of scientific or mechanical training. When this ability is coupled with practical knowledge and a scientific background, it almost always succeeds.

A deterring factor to all aeronautical development is the question of cost. Many able men have excellent ideas which they would put into practice were they not limited financially. Up to the present, only governments have been able to foot the bills for the solution of the greater problems. These often depend on political expediency and the financial interests involved. It is exemplified particularly in the development of aviation in the United States, where it has been consistently opposed by those interested in the continuance of the obsolete battleship, because it uses a great deal of steel and fuel and necessitates the maintenance of great shipyards. Without doubt, when passenger-carrying aircraft become an economic necessity, they will be opposed by the railroads, bus lines and in some cases steamship companies, who will not like to see their passengers taken away from them. Already in the United States, the Navy and the transportation interests have taken hold of aviation, bag and baggage, so as to control it for their own advantage, greatly to its detriment. Any new development has to take these things into consideration.

There is no apparent limit to the size, carrying

capacity or speed of an airship. The bigger they are, the more economical they become, because where great volumes of lifting gas are used in large containers, the weight of the structure per unit of cubical contents is less. Small ones carry comparatively small loads, but as they are made larger the ratio of the weight carried increases in greater proportion, until an airship about four times the size of the Graf Zeppelin is reached, when the peak of efficiency is obtained. After this, the performance remains about the same for any size built. Within the next thirty years we may reasonably expect to see airships 2000 feet long and 800 feet in diameter, carrying hundreds of passengers and practically impervious to any accidents of weather or temperature.

With equipment that is now being worked out, airships can be built that will cross the Atlantic in from twenty-four to thirty-six hours. A passenger might go to a future air station in the center of New York City, be transported through an underground tube to the airport and placed on board an airship at ten o'clock at night, which would leave immediately for London, Paris or Berlin at a speed of one hundred miles an hour or more. When he awoke, he would be halfway across the ocean, and that night would have reached his destination. All continents, countries or islands in the seas could be reached by this form of transportation.

As the airship flies along, mail, express or passengers can be delivered to it by airplanes, which may land or hook on the ship. Or the airship can put out a cable to which these things can be attached from the ground, or other aircraft. An airship can hover over a place and discharge its passengers without landing, either by means of airplanes, gliders, parachutes or lowering them on cables.

In war, airships could be formed into fleets for carrying airplanes, which could fly out from them on various missions and be guided back by radio. They could be refueled and repaired on the airship. These airships would be completely equipped with cannon and machine guns, chemical weapons, and bombs and torpedoes that may be shot out and their direction controlled by radio.

The speed of heavier-than-air craft will be much greater than airships, and they will act as the rapid distributors of passengers and goods while the airships will carry the heavy freight for long distances.

The passenger airplane of the future will have a span of one hundred and fifty feet or more. Its wings, sixteen feet thick, will have a chord of fifty feet, the interior being fitted up with cabins, recreation rooms, kitchens, dining rooms, bathrooms, all properly ventilated and heated. The power plant will consist of Diesel heavy oil engines, six or eight in number, placed on the center line of the craft. This will concentrate the weight so as to give the greatest stability possible to the craft. The fuel, which will be practically non-inflammable, will be contained in a series of tanks covered with crash-proof material, arranged so that they may be thrown out of the craft by a pull on a single lever, in case of accident in the air or if it is desired to lighten the ship for a forced landing.

The landing gear, which may be drawn up into the body of the plane when in flight, will have wheels fifteen feet or more in diameter, able to roll over any ordinary fence, ditch or large undulation in the ground, and equipped with brakes. The tailskid, also retractable, will be in the form of a wheel, also equipped with a brake.

The engines will drive through gearing on one big propellor, twenty-five or thirty feet in diameter, which will turn at about 850 revolutions a minute, the most efficient speed. It will be able to get out beyond the eddies and dead air around the wings and grip the good air, where it will give the maximum pull.

In flight, this airplane will look like one big wing

The New Junkers 2400 H.P. Airplane G-38 Constructed Entirely of Metal with Wings Eight Feet Thick. It Measures 75 Feet 5 Inches in Length with a Wing Span of 147 Feet 6 Inches

Another View of the New Junkers Airplane G-38

FUTURE AVIATION

which is all lifting surface, with a fuselage merely large enough and long enough to support the tail surfaces necessary for control. It will have a speed of from 300 to 500 miles per hour. Gyroscopic controls will fly it straight through storms and fogs, and it will be provided with a means of landing in fog. It will be equipped with radio telegraph and telephone so that the crew or passengers may talk to the ground at any time. Its body will be watertight, so that in case a landing is made on the water, it can float indefinitely. Passengers will be equipped with parachutes and life preservers made up in the form of comfortable vests, which may be worn at all times in flight.

The navigating personnel of the plane will be placed far enough back so that the pilot can see the wing of his ship, which will facilitate leveling his machine either on the horizon or by the instruments on his board. His seat will be so constructed that he may be lifted up whenever he desires to feel the air, instead of being sealed up inside a closed cabin where he must rely solely on instruments. Most of the crashes that result when a big airplane stalls may be blamed on the practice of enclosing the pilot and placing him too far forward so that he cannot get the feel of the ship.

An airplane such as this, built entirely of metal,

will need no hangars or shelter but can remain outside in all kinds of weather. Repairs can be made on it while it is in flight as well as on the ground. There will be comparatively little deterioration to such a plane and it will last for years. Smaller airplanes will be built on similar lines. Aircraft for use around cities or over restricted areas will use the principle of the autogyro or helicopter and be able to land on roofs or back lots. It will be a long time before everyone is able to use aircraft in the way the automobile is used now, because as at present constructed, certain physical and mental characteristics not possessed by everyone are required for their operation.

The development of air navigation which has already taken place makes it possible for an airplane to find its way from one place to another with absolute certainty, no matter what meteorological conditions exist. We only lack an instrument that will tell constantly how far the earth is under the airplane, and will indicate the general character of the earth and the direction in which it is sloped, also if the airplane is passing over obstructions such as trees, houses, telegraph or high power lines.

Speeds of four hundred miles an hour can be attained at present, and I see no apparent limit

The Little Eight H.P. Plane That Flew from Dayton to Columbus, Ohio, One Hundred and Eighty Miles, on Two and One-Half Gallons of Gasoline

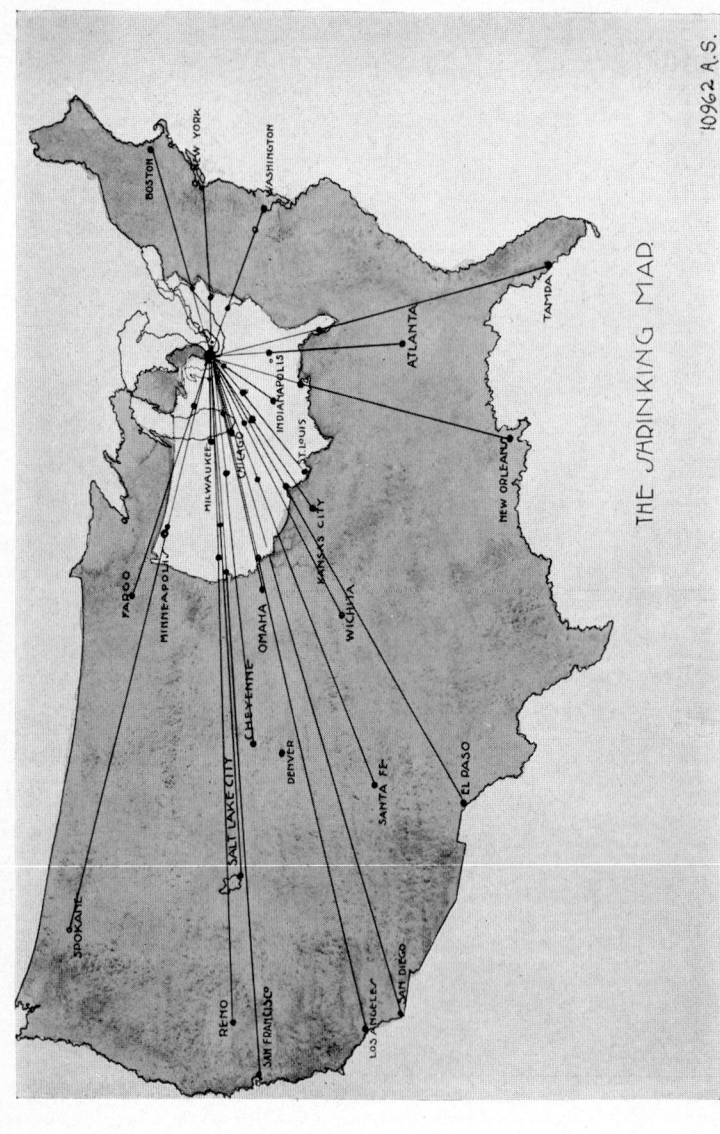

The Large Map Indicates the Size of the United States when Rail or Motor Transportation Was the Fastest Means of Travel. The Smaller Map Shows the Country when Aircraft Have Reduced the Time Element

FUTURE AVIATION

to speed in the air except fusion, such as a meteor is subjected to when it comes into contact with the atmosphere of earth after its journey through space. Airplanes can be built today that will take passengers, mail and express from New York to San Francisco at the rate of three hundred miles an hour and make it in one jump, in other words an eight or ten hour trip between the two cities.

In case of war, the large airplane described above can be transformed into a bomber or transport ship within twenty-four hours. It will have a cruising radius of from five to seven thousand miles. Heavier-than-air craft will hit the quick decisive blows, while lighter-than-air ships will act as floating air islands on which the airplanes can refuel and refit themselves.

Aviation is and will continue to be the principal arm of national defense. So great is the military advantage accruing to a strong air power that it might easily achieve world dominion. All parts of the world can be communicated with instantly by radio or wire. Aviation has not only reduced the size of the world to one-sixth its former dimensions, but has effaced all natural barriers to transportation. Every part of it, no matter whether over land or sea, desert or arctic waste, is accessible to aircraft.

[THE END]

INDEX

Index

Absolute Zero, 299
Aerial photography, 159
Aeronautical Insurance, 117
Afghanistan, 238
Africa, 233
Afridis, 238
Aguinaldo, General, 210, 211
Air Commerce Act, 295
Alaska, 7, 155, 260
Aleutian Island, 73
Alexander the Great, 227
Allegheny Mountains, 80, 152, 207
Allies, 243
America, 30, 224
American Army, 210
Amsterdam, 233
Apple Tree Johnny, 205
Arctic regions, 73, 120
Arctic Siberia, 246
Armengaud, General, 240
Armistice, 210, 244, 287
Army War College, 9
Austria, 233, 235
Asia, 29, 30, 155, 213
Atlanta, 114
Atlantic Ocean, 73

Baltic Sea, 220, 226
Baluchistan, 238
Bangkok, 250
Belgium, 235, 240
Bennett, James Gordon, Balloon races, 223
Bering Sea, 73
Berlin, Germany, 217, 218, 227, 271
Binghamton, New York, 78
Bissell, Lieutenant, 198, 200, 201, 207
Blue Ridge Mountains, 80, 176
Bolling Field, 176, 208
Borneo, 250
Borodino, 226, 227
Boston, 113
British Air Force, 238
British Board of Trade, 290

British Imperial Airway System, 232
British Isles, 236
"B-Wright," 58

Camp Borden, Canada, 198, 199, 200
Camp Stotsenburg, 211
Canadian Air Force, 200
Canary Islands, 155
Cape Finisterre, Spain, 155
Carpathian Mountains, 226
Caspian Sea, 246
Caucasus, 247, 248
Central America, 280
Chanute, 8, 23
Chesapeake Bay, 79, 207
Chicago, 92, 93, 99, 207
China, 251
China Sea, 258
Christie, Captain, 198, 200
Cierva autogyro, 25
Civil War, 184, 245, 254
Cleveland, 114
Coast Guard, 260
Confederate Army, 254
Conflans, 282
Constitution, 294
Count Zeppelin, 184, 185, 187, 245, 246
Crimea, 247
Curtiss, Glenn, 9
Czecho-Slovakia, 240

Daimler, 31
Dantzig, 220, 221
Dayton, Ohio, 102, 103, 176
Denmark, 245
Department of Commerce, 290
Deruluft, 229
Detroit, Michigan, 41, 202, 207
Deutsch de la Meurthe, 184
Diesel engine, 37, 38, 41
Dornier flying boat, 244
Drachenfels, 210
Dumont, Santos, 184
Dwina River, 222

[311]

INDEX

East Indies, 250
East Prussia, 221
East River, 297
Eckener, Doctor, 246
Egypt, 184
El Paso, Texas, 208, 209
England, 216, 235
English Channel, 235, 286
Equator, 159
Eskimos, 246
Essen, 223, 278
Eubanks, Lieutenant, 204
Euphrates rivers, 237
Europe, 30, 93, 217

"Farmer's Weather Almanacs," 86
First Pursuit Group, 199
Fisher, Mr. Carl, 102
Fokker, German, 284
France, 28, 184, 235, 239, 240
French Army, 240, 241
French Revolution, 181
Friedrichshafen, 180

Gaul, 242
Germany, 38, 163, 185, 235
Good Pasture River, 7
Gotha, German, 287, 288
Graf Zeppelin, 180, 187, 246, 302
Great Britain, 238
Great Circle, 127
Great Lakes, 73
Greenland, 73, 155, 260
Gulf Stream, 73, 88
"Gypsy pilots," 170

Hagood, General, 211, 212
Handley-Page, English, 232, 288
Handley-Page wing slot, 143
Hanney, Colonel, 208
Hartney, Col., 176, 177
Hawaii, 160, 203
Hay fever, 70
Helium, 189
Holland, 235
Hudson river, 297
Huns, 222

Iceland, 260
Illinois, 223
Immelmann turn, 172, 173
India, 237, 238

Indianapolis, 102
Indo-China, 241
International Boundary, 199
Iraq, 237, 240
Ireland, 155
Island of Newfoundland, 155
Italy, 235, 241
Italian Air Force, 243
Ithaca, New York, 76

Jacksonville, Florida, 99
Japan, 248, 249
Java, 213, 250
Jenghiz Khan, 247
Junkers, The, 42, 244, 245

Kaiser, 224
Kansas, 223
Koenigsberg, 221, 223, 224, 229
Kovno, 222
Krim, Abd-el, 240, 241

Labrador, 260
Lakehurst, New Jersey, 180
Lake Huron, 199, 202
Lake St. Clair, 199, 202, 203
Langley Field, Virginia, 41, 69, 81
Langley, Prof., 8
Laplanders, 246
Le Bourget, 231
Leavenworth, Fort, 8
Liberty engines, 228
Lilienthal, 8, 23
Lincoln Highway, 101, 102
Lithuania, Republic of, 221
Logan, Lieut., 177
London, 231, 235, 244
Long Island, 76, 93
Lorelie, 210
Los Angeles, 114
Lowe, Professor, 184
Lucas, King, 212
Lufthansa, 243
Luzon Island, 210, 211

Madagascar, 241
Maitland, Lieut., 76, 78
Manchuria, 212
Manhattan Island, 297
Marines, 260
Mariveles Mountain, 210
Marseilles, 233
Mars la Tour, 282

[312]

INDEX

Mayon Volcano, 211
McClelland, General, 184
McGill University, Canada, 79
Mediterranean, 233, 242, 258
Merkle, Mr., 229
Mexico, 280
Middle Ages, 32, 255, 273
Military flyer, 63
Milling, Lieut., 58
Milwaukee, 93, 207
Minsk, 222
Mitchel Field, Long Island, 78
Mitchell, Mrs., 202, 203, 211
Mongolia, 247
Monongahela Valley, 165
Montgolfier, 28
Morocco, 240, 243
Moscow, Russia, 217, 218, 224, 226, 227, 228
Moselle River, 210
Moundsville, West Virginia, 205, 206
Mukden, 212
Mussolini, 241

Napoleon, 184, 226
"Naverisk," 8
Negritos, 211
Newcomb, Prof. Simon, 8
New Orleans, 205
Newport News, 9
New York, 47, 93, 99, 205, 302
Neuweid, 210
Nieuports, 171

Oahu, 203
Ochney airdome, 288
Ocker, Major, 177
Ohio River, 105
"Order of the Dead Horse," 212
Otto, 31

Pacific Ocean, 73
Packard engine, 38, 41
Parachute, The, 138
Paris, 181, 231, 244
Peking, 155, 247
Philadelphia, 93, 165
Philippines, 210
Phoenician system, 257
Pinsk, 222
Pittsburgh, 114, 165, 262
Poland, 240

Porto Rico, 8
Postmaster General, 113
Potomac, 9, 153, 208
President of the United States, 153
Prince of Wales, 210
Pripet swamps, 222

R-36, 187
Reich, 243
Rhine, 210, 278
Rice, Senator, 160
Richmond, Virginia, 254
Riffs, 241
Rocky Mountains, 175
Romans, 242
Royal Air Force, 236
Russia, 222, 223, 224, 225, 227, 229, 235
Russian Army, 224

Sacramento Mountains, 208
Saint Sauveur, 227
Salt Lake City, 114
Samarkand, 248
San Diego, California, 180
San Domingo, 155
San Francisco, 47, 93, 102
San Juan Harbor, 8
Sarawak, 250
Scandinavia, 260
Sea of Aral, 246
Selfridge Field, 203
Shenandoah, 82, 187
Siam, 213, 250
Siberia, 155, 260
Smolensk, 224, 225
Soviet Republic, 217, 246
Spad airplanes, 171
Spain, 235, 243
Ste. Claire River, 202
St. Elizabeth's Insane Asylum, 198
Stick, The, 52
St. Mihiel, 100, 261
Straits of Malacca, 258
Strasbourg in Alsace, 233
Strong, Major, 69
Suez Canal, 258
Sweden, 245
Switzerland, 242

Taal Volcano, 211
Tamerlane, 248
Tartars, 222

INDEX

Temperate Zone, 159
Templehofer Field, 218
Tigris River, 237
Tokyo, Japan, 180
Toul, 288
Treaty of Versailles, 243, 244
Tso-Lin, Marshal Chang, 212, 213
Turkestan, 246, 247
Turkey, 233

Union Army, 254
United French Airlines, 232
United States, 38, 216
U. S. Air Mail Service, 112

Vesuvius, 211

Virginia, 222
Vladivostock, 247
Von Opel, Franz, 45

Washington, 103, 152, 208, 254
Waziri, 238
White Sea, 247
Wicomico River, 208
Woodruff, 198, 201, 205
World War, 195, 254, 259, 264
Wright Brothers, 8, 23, 24

Zanesville, Ohio, 152
Zeppelin, 29, 187
Zeppelin, Count, 8
Zeppelin Foundation, 245, 246